ACTIVITY BOOK

FOR STUDENTS AND TEACHERS

Steps to Discovering Wind and Water

KARINA YOUNK

Art Image Publications

Thoughtsteps is an intermediate learning resource based on the integration of language arts, science, and social studies, along with other subject areas and processing skills, whenever there are natural links. *Thoughtsteps* can be used with the entire class, with small groups, with individual students, or as a learning centre.

EDITORS:
Catherine Stewart
Andrew Vandal
Maryse Bérubé

STUDENT EDITORS:
Shannon Provencher
Alexandre Fallon

STYLISTIC EDITING:
Joan Irving

PILOT CLASSES:
Cathie Eck, Grade 4/5
Quarterway Elementary, Nanaimo, B.C.
Katya Roy, Grade 7
Pauline Haarer Elementary, Nanaimo, B.C.

CONSULTANTS IN MUSIC AND ART:
Sue Postans
Regan Rasmussen
Claude Vallières

ISBN: 1-896876-08-0

CANADA
Art Image Publications Inc.
3281 Jean-Beraud Avenue
Laval, QC
H7T 2L2
Tel: (514) 334-5912
     1 800 361-4504
Fax: (514) 688-6269

U.S.A.
Art Image Publications Inc.
61 Main Street
P.O. Box 568
Champlain, N.Y. 12919
Tel: 1 800 361-2598
Fax: (518) 298-5433

Printed in Canada

TABLE OF CONTENTS

Parts of Thoughtsteps — 5

Between Earth and Sky — 7

Let's Construct a Hot Air Balloon — 8

How Does It Fly? — 12

Researching Lighter-than-air Craft — 16

Imagine Interviewing a Pioneer of Flight! — 22

My Game's a Washout! — 23

Games for Rainy Days — 24

Ways of Adapting to the Weather — 28

My Baseball Game's a Washout! — 34

A Home-Made Weather Station — 40

The Muscles of the Sun and Wind — 48

Tales Told by Water — 53

Tell Me of Your Travels, Water! — 54

Come Swim My Cycle — 60

Hello Raindrop! Where Have You Been? — 70

All that Water Just for Me? — 80

Making Careers Out of Water — 84

Organizing and Hosting a Festival — 85

Resources for Discovering Wind and Water — 94

Thoughtsteps

SO YOU'RE GETTING READY TO WANDER THROUGH *THOUGHTSTEPS*?

Before you start, check out these pieces of information:

p.5 - The parts of *Thoughtsteps*.

p.6 - How to make *Thoughtsteps* work for you by using the *Thoughtsteps Map* and *Thoughtsteps Planner*.

p.7 - Preparing your *Thoughtsteps Journal* and using the *Steps to Discovering...* activities.

PARTS OF *THOUGHTSTEPS*

First, let's look at the six components or parts of *Thoughtsteps*. You prepare one part (your journal or notebook) and the other five parts are provided for you in the centres. These six components are:

1. The *Thoughtsteps Journal* is your personal binder containing your projects, notes, written work, experiments, evaluations, and more. The journal becomes your record of what you accomplish and learn as you work through the centres and themes in *Thoughtsteps.*

2. The *Thoughtsteps Map* is a map showing the different paths or options that a learner may choose. The map may seem confusing if you try to read the whole thing at once, but if you follow one path from start to finish, you'll soon understand how the map works.

3. The *Thoughtsteps Planner* is a folder containing a summary of the concepts and skills you will be learning in each theme of a centre. Its purpose is to help you determine which activities you will be doing as a class, as a small group, or as

an individual. It is like an itinerary for a trip, which tells you in advance what you will be expected to collect, learn, or observe for each part of your journey.

It can also help you with your evaluation of the theme, and what you learned. At the end of each activity, you will review the objectives and ask yourself if you have accomplished what you set out to do.

4. The *Thoughtsteps Toolbox* contains a series of cards with information and evaluation notes designed to help you learn HOW to do something.

5. *Steps to Discovering...* is a guide for working your way through the projects and activities, contained in each centre or theme. When you read through your *Steps to Discovering...* activities, you'll choose a path and follow the suggestions along the way. *Steps* will help you decide WHAT to do, WHERE to look, WHO you're working with (alone, in a group, or as a class), WHEN you need to record information, and WHY you're doing the activity. Like a tour book, it helps you pick and choose not only your destination but also what you plan to do along the way. Like any tour, you might like to "go it alone", travel with a friend, or have someone, like your teacher or a group leader, help you plan your way.

6. *Discovering Wind and Water; Discovering Culture and Values; Discovering the Earth's Crust; Discovering Space;* etc. are some of the resource books in the *Thoughtsteps* series. They contain stories, poems, artwork, projects, experiments and much more to give you a starting point for information on the centres and themes.

Using the *Thoughtsteps Map* and the *Thoughtsteps Planner*

Have you ever juggled before? Juggling one or two objects is easy. Juggling more objects takes skill and practice. Once you know how *Thoughtsteps* works, you'll be able to juggle its components easily.

Thoughtsteps **is set up so that you take one step at a time. Just follow the directions listed below.**

N.B. To be ready to discuss the centre as a group, post the *Thoughtsteps Map* in a place where it will stay for the duration of your work with this centre. Have the group members sit so that they can see the *Thoughtsteps Map*. Distribute the *Thoughtsteps Planners*, the folders for the themes in the centre, to each member of the group.

---

1. Look at the *Thoughtsteps Map*. What is the name of the centre you will be working in, *Discovering Wind and Water*; *Discovering Space*; or *Discovering...?*
2. Each *Thoughtsteps* centre contains two or more options for themes and a culminating cooperative project integrating the activities from all the themes. For example, in *Discovering Wind and Water*, the choices are: air; weather; water. What are your options in the centre you have chosen? What would you like to learn about? Below each option on the *Thoughtsteps Map* is the title of the theme. For now, find the title of the Cooperative Project.
3. Below each theme on the *Thoughtsteps Map* are several titles for the different learning **paths** that you may follow. Follow the **path** below the Cooperative Project.

4. What do you need to do to prepare for this path? Check the **preparation section** of your *Thoughtsteps Map*. What are you expected to learn? The *Thoughtsteps Planner* describes the learning objectives for each theme and subject area. Check the preparation objectives 𝒫 for the Cooperative Project.
5. What will you be producing or doing? Check the **action or activity section** of your map. Check your *Thoughtsteps Planner* for the activity objectives 𝒜.
6. What are your options for extending the activity? Check the **extension section** of the map. These objectives aren't listed beside 𝐸 in your *Thoughtsteps Planner*, but if you select one of these activities, your teacher has a list of the objectives in the *Educator's Planner*.
7. What are you asked to think about or reflect on at the end of your activity? Check the **reflection section** of your map and the reflection objectives 𝑅 in your *Thoughtsteps Planner*.
8. When you are ready to work on a path, refer to the appropriate *Steps to Discovering...* activity book. It contains all the information you will need (explanations for the activities, the *Toolbox* cards, etc.). The **STEPS**... page is indicated below each path title on the *Thoughtsteps Map*. If you are planning to do a Cooperative Project, consult the pages in your *Steps to Discovering...* book now. You will need to complete the preparation stage of this project before planning your other activities for this centre.
9. Once you have examined the *Thoughtsteps Map* and the Cooperative Project, select the activities you will do as a whole class, in small groups, or individually. Mark your *Thoughtsteps Planner* accordingly: **C; G; I**. If there are activities that you won't be doing in class, you may decide to do these on your own. Mark these in your *Planner* as well.

STEPS TO DISCOVERING... ACTIVITIES

Preparing your *Thoughtsteps Journal*

A

Between Earth and Sky

 Open your *Thoughtsteps Journal*. Add to it a blank page, a lined page, and two more blank pages.
- On the first page, write the title of your theme.
- On the lined page, write the words "Table of Contents". As you work through the theme, list your activities here.
- On the next blank page, list your ideas, words, knowledge relating to hot air balloons, flight, festivals, and air. See **Tool A2**.

 Using your list of ideas from the brainstorming activity, make a poster on the next page of your *Thoughtsteps Journal*. Show words and images about the theme *Discovering Wind and Water*: **Between Earth and Sky**.

On the back side of this page, write the title "Discovering New Words". As you work through the activities in this theme, list on this page any new words you encounter.

E.1 Use a dictionary to review spelling.

Or

E.2 Create a class poster combining everyone's ideas.

Or

E.3 Look through other resource books for ideas for illustrations or words. Add them to your poster.

Or

E.4 Add illustrations to your title page.

Or

E.5 Add a **Bibliography** page. See **Tool A5** to learn how to list your sources.

R Check your poster for spelling. Remember it's a tool you will use during the entire theme! Does it represent the theme? At the bottom of the poster, write down three ideas you would like to explore in this theme.

A

Between Earth and Sky

A.1

Let's Construct a Hot Air Balloon

(LA: Identify/ use information from a text to gather details for a poster and to complete a papier-mâché model. Analyse a written text to demonstrate the use of quotation marks.)

Read the story, "The Hot Air Balloon Festival", **pages 5** to **7** of *Discovering Wind and Water*. Refer to the questions from **Tool C1.** As you read, or when you are finished reading, you may wish to add new words to your vocabulary poster. Observe how quotation marks were used in the story. Then, in your *Thoughtsteps Journal*, rewrite the conversation shown on **STEPSpage 10** adding the missing quotation marks. Refer to **Tool E4** for help if needed.

(FA: Create a model of an inanimate object using papier-mâché. Use colour, shade, and shape to create a drawing of a 3-D object. LA: Write an imaginary dialogue using quotation marks.)

Construct your model hot air balloon out of papier-mâché following the directions on **pages 7, 8** and **9** of *Discovering Wind and Water*. These pages tell you what materials you will need. If you think your nacelle may need to be a different size, follow the extension activity described below and on **STEPSpage 11.**

Once you have constructed your balloon, imagine what it would be like to fly over your home, your school, or the place of your dreams, in your hot air balloon. Draw a bird's-eye view of what you would see below. Then, write a dialogue between two people as they drift through the skies (you might be one of them). Display your balloon, your illustration, and your dialogue. You might decide to work with a partner and present your dialogue in the form of a skit. Use **Tools E4** and **C8** to edit your dialogue.

E.1 (Ma: Use metric units to measure distances and area. Construct 2- and 3-D figures. Compare and use formulas for area and volume. Establish relationships between length and width to reduce or enlarge figures.)

Change the proportions of your nacelle. Refer to **Tool E6** and try changing the size of your nacelle following the directions on **STEPSpage 11.**

Or

E.2 (FA: Create a collage. Use colour, shade, and shape to create symbolism, focus, or dominance.)

Prepare a collage of "All that flies" to commemorate (celebrate) the success of the Montgolfier brothers and other inventors. (You can use people, animals, machines and so on, e.g., Mary Poppins, Pegasus, Icarus, a supersonic jet.) See **Tool D3** for directions.

Or

E.3 (FA: Create a sculpture. Use colour, shade, and shape to create 3-D rounded objects.)

Prepare a stuffed hot air balloon or create your own technique for designing a hot air balloon. See **Tool D8** for ideas or directions. If you create your own hot air balloon, write down the instructions so that someone else might use your technique. Your description could be posted in the class or kept in your *Thoughtsteps Journal*.

A

Between
Earth
and Sky

A.1

*Let's
Construct
a Hot Air
Balloon*

E.4 (FA: Experiment with creative visualization.)
Use the text from **STEPSpage 10,** or your own dialogue from the activity stage, to perform a creative visualization exercise. Have the participants sit or lie comfortably, eyes closed, as you read your dialogue to them. Use **Tool B2** to prepare your presentations.

R (SD: Identify and develop means of improving effective expression and communication. FA: Express an opinion regarding a personal work of art.)
Using **Tool A9**, add your project evaluation comments to your *Thoughtsteps Journal*. Focus your answers on how well you expressed and communicated your ideas in the three different formats: balloon, dialogue, and illustration. You might want to include a snapshot or an illustration of your balloon or of your other creations.

If you used other **Toolbox** cards, complete the corresponding evaluation forms and include them in your *Thoughtsteps Journal*.

USE QUOTATION MARKS IN A CONVERSATION

(LA: Analyse a written text to demonstrate the use of quotation marks.)

Refer to **Tool E4** and write this conversation in your *Thoughtsteps Journal* adding the missing quotation marks.

Who Said What?

The sun was hot that day as I was walking in the forest. I was really thirsty. Right next to the path, there was a small stream. As I leaned forward to drink from the stream, a shadow crept over me.

I screamed, What's happening?

At the same instant, I heard a loud noise behind me.
I turned around. Two enormous multi-coloured eyes were staring down at me. There was a gigantic head just above the trees.

I yelled, Help! Somebody save me!

There was no answer. The huge head floated slowly toward me, not saying a word. I backed up to get away and, splish! splash!, I found myself sitting in the stream.

At that moment I heard a voice say, Hey! Martin! Did you hear that noise? It sounded like someone falling in water.

Blow a little more hot air into the balloon, another voice replied. Let's go take a look!

I said to myself, Is this beast talking to some other beast?

Again there was a loud noise. The head started to rise in the air and to move toward me.

I whispered to myself, Oh no! It's coming to get me!

I closed my eyes. I was too afraid to look.

Hey, you, a stern voice called down. What are you doing sitting in a brook?

I opened my eyes ever so slowly. Now I had to shield them from the sun. I looked up and saw… a majestic hot air balloon with two multi-coloured eyes rising in the sky above me.

I have never told this story to anyone. People would laugh at me!

CHANGE THE PROPORTIONS (SIZE) OF YOUR NACELLE

(Ma: Use metric units to measure distances and area. Construct 2- and 3-D figures. Compare and use formulas for area and volume. Establish relationships between length and width to reduce or enlarge figures.)

Is your nacelle too big or too small for your hot air balloon? So change it. Simply change the size or the area of the square you are using in your pattern. Here are a few hints to help you do this:

In *Discovering Wind and Water*, **page 9**, the square described has dimensions (a size) of 5 cm x 5 cm for a total area of _____ cm². One way of illustrating the area of your square would be to divide it into square centimetres like this:

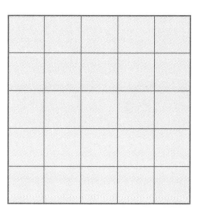

To change the dimensions of your square, you could simply add or subtract one or more rows and an equal number of columns like this:

4 cm x 4 cm = an area of _____ cm²   6 cm x 6 cm = an area of _____ cm²

What would be the area of a square 7 cm x 7 cm or a square 12 cm x 12 cm?

Could you build a new cube using dimensions different from the one described in the book? Remember that if you change the area of one face of the cube, you have to change the area of the other five faces of the cube. Otherwise, you will no longer have a cube!

Could you calculate (figure out) the total area of your nacelle if you needed to cover it with material or paper?

A
Between
Earth
and Sky

A.1

Let's
Construct
a Hot Air
Balloon

A

Between Earth and Sky

A.2

How Does It Fly?

(Sc: Create a hypothesis by asking questions.)

In a small group, or with the entire class, discuss how some objects are able to float in air by answering these questions:
- How could air lift a stone?
- What objects will float in air?
- Why is it that some objects will float and others require lifting?

From your discussion, are there new words about air that you could add to your vocabulary list in your *Thoughtsteps Journal*?

Refer to the evaluation form for **Tool C5** to learn what a hypothesis is. Before you look, can you guess? In your *Thoughtsteps Journal*, write a hypothesis in answer to one or more of the above questions.

(LA: Identify/use information from a text to select pertinent details and to experiment with the message. Sc: Use the scientific process to identify and compare the physical properties of matter.)

Read the first two experiments on **pages 10** and **11** of *Discovering Wind and Water*. Using **Tool C5** and the experiments on **pages 10** and **11** of *Discovering Wind and Water*, look at how reports are written on experiments. Try at least one of the four experiments on **pages 10** to **13** of *Discovering Wind and Water*. Write a report on each of the experiments you try and include them in your *Thoughtsteps Journal*. Don't forget to date your work!

Writing the conclusion for an experiment is probably the most important step. Using the model from **Tool C5**, evaluate your conclusions to be sure you have included the necessary information.

E.1 (LA: Identify/use information from a text to select pertinent details and to experiment with the message. Sc: Use the scientific process to identify and compare the physical properties of matter.)

Experiment with the density of water using the experiments on **STEPSpages 13, 14** and **15** and **Tool C5**. How are the properties of air (what air is like) similar to, or different from, the properties of water?

(SD: Identify, develop, and sustain means of improving problem-solving skills.)

After doing several experiments on a similar topic, it is important to stop and record what you know about the topic. Using the experiments you tried, explain what you know now about the following topics:
- the properties of air;
- the effect of temperature on air;
- what variables enable an object to float in the air;
- the kinds of objects that can be lifted by hot air.

Record your comments in your *Thoughtsteps Journal.*

.1 EXPERIMENT WITH THE DENSITY OF WATER

(LA: Identify/use information from a text to select pertinent details and to experiment with the message. Sc: Use the scientific process to identify and compare the physical properties of matter.)
Try the following experiments and record your results using **Tool C5**.

Experiment 1: Double Densities

MATERIALS:

• 2 large containers	• food colouring or ink
• 2 small flasks or bottles	• boiling water and ice water

PROCEDURE:

1. Fill one container with hot water and the other with ice water.
2. Fill one flask with hot water and the other with ice water.
3. Add a few drops of food colouring to each flask (e.g., red to the hot water and blue to the cold water).
4. Pour a little of the hot water along the sides of the container of cold water. Observe the two types of water as they mix.
5. Repeat step 4 pouring the cold water into the container of hot water and observe how they mix.

OBSERVATIONS:

What happens to the coloured water?

CONCLUSION:

In liquid form, do hot and cold water have the same density? Which one rises to the surface? Which one sinks to the bottom?

Experiment 2: Tea Cubes Anyone?

MATERIALS:
- a large transparent container
- cold water
- an ice cube made with tea or coffee

PROCEDURE:
1. Fill the container with cold water.
2. Place the ice cube in the container.
3. Observe the movement of the liquid underneath the ice cube as it melts.

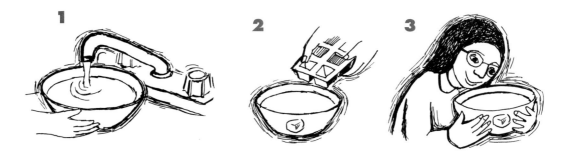

OBSERVATIONS:
What happens to the water from the ice cube?
Can you draw the movement of the ice water?

CONCLUSION:
Do cold water and hot water occupy the same volume or area?
Describe why you think the ice water moved the way it did?
Can you think of another way to do this experiment?

Sidebar:

A

Between Earth and Sky

A.2

How Does It Fly?

Experiment 3: Genie in a Bottle

MATERIALS:
- a large container
- a small bottle
- hot water tinted with food colouring, tea, or ink
- old water
- 30 cm of string

PROCEDURE:
1. Fill the large container half full with cold water.
2. Attach the string to the bottle.
3. Fill the bottle with the hot coloured water.
4. Immerse the bottle in the cold water, using the string to hold it.
5. Observe the movement of the coloured liquid.

1

2

3

4

5

OBSERVATIONS:
What happens to the water in the bottle?

CONCLUSION:
In liquid form, which is more dense, hot water or cold water?

A
Between Earth and Sky

A.3
Researching Lighter-than-air Craft

(LA: Develop strategies to analyse media information quickly. Identify/use information gathered from notes to select pertinent details and to organize them logically in the form of a simple research report. Demonstrate an understanding of language conventions and mechanics. Sc: Examine the contributions/impact of science/technology in societies.)

Read the text "The Success of the Montgolfier Brothers" on **pages 16** and **17** of *Discovering Wind and Water*. As you read, take notes by recording the key pieces of information on a puzzle frame like the one shown in the example on **STEPSpage 18**. In paragraph form, write a more detailed description of the information contained in your puzzle.

You may need to work on forming good sentences and paragraphs; **STEPSpage 19** gives two examples of summaries. Using **Tools E3** and **E4** as a guide, rewrite these two texts using the correct punctuation and paragraph indentations.

(LA: Develop strategies to analyse media information quickly. Identify/use information gathered from notes to select pertinent details and to organize them logically in the form of a simple research report. Demonstrate an understanding of language conventions and mechanics. Sc: Examine the contributions/impact of science/technology in societies.)

Prepare a puzzle and an information text about another "lighter-than-air craft" or another invention in aeronautics using the following steps:

- Use **Tool A3** and the questions on **STEPSpage 20** to help you choose a topic;

- Prepare a list of questions that you want to research. See **Tool A4**. Record your questions on a puzzle frame like the one shown on **STEPSpage 18**. Photocopy or trace your puzzle frame. After locating the information, record the answers to your questions on your puzzle frame and complete it by following the directions on **STEPSpage 18**. See **Tool A5**;

- Write a summary in paragraph form of the information contained in your puzzle. Depending on the depth of your project, this may be your entire project or simply the introductory paragraph. The paragraph may be shared with others. Ask them to read your paragraph then complete the puzzle by answering the questions in the frame. If this paragraph was simply the introduction to your research, the note below is intended for you.
Remember that it is helpful to decide how you would like to present your research (video, display, timeline, story, play, etc.) before writing down your project.

N.B. A research project is made up of several steps. This is where your **Toolbox** cards can help. Look at the **Table of Contents**. The cards in section **A. *Thoughtsteps* for Metacognition** and **Tool C4** can help you plan and organize your research project. **Tool C8** is useful if you want to edit what you have written. Review these sections now or as you progress in your research.

E.1 (Ma: Construct/interpret a number line. SS: Represent a series of events on a timeline. Organize a series of events chronologically.)

Sequence a series of events on a timeline using the sample on **STEPSpage 21**. **Tool D7** can help you get started.

OR

E.2 (Ma: Construct/interpret a number line. SS: Represent a series of events on a timeline. Organize a series of events chronologically. Sc: Explore the functions of air/space craft. Understand how engines function. FA: Create a mural to illustrate a sequence of events.)

Combine the data from all of the research projects onto a timeline in the form of a mural in your classroom. Or, simply construct a timeline for your own research and include it in your *Thoughtsteps Journal*. See **Tools D3** and **D7**.

 (SD: Understand the importance of change as a process for improving development.)

Use **Tool C4** or **A9** to help you reflect on your research project. If you used other **Toolbox** cards, complete the corresponding evaluation forms and include them in your *Thoughtsteps Journal*.

A

Between Earth and Sky

A.3

Researching Lighter-than-air Craft

A

Between
Earth
and Sky

A.3

*Researching
Lighter-
than-air
Craft*

TAKE NOTES AND DESIGN A JIG-SAW PUZZLE

(LA: Develop strategies to analyse media information quickly. Identify/use information gathered from notes to select pertinent details and to organize them logically in the form of a simple research report. Demonstrate an understanding of language conventions and mechanics. Sc: Examine the contributions/impact of science/ technology in societies.)

One way to take notes is to record the key pieces of information in separate boxes or sections of a page as in the puzzle example below.

Trace this puzzle pattern onto a piece of paper. Write the answers to each question in the correct space on your paper. When you have finished, glue your paper to a piece of cardboard. Draw and colour a picture of the inventor or the invention on the other side of the cardboard. Cut out your puzzle and place the pieces with the answers facing up. Answer each question on this page using your puzzle pieces. Flip your answer piece over so the picture side is showing and place it over top of the question. Exchange pieces with a friend and do each other's puzzles.

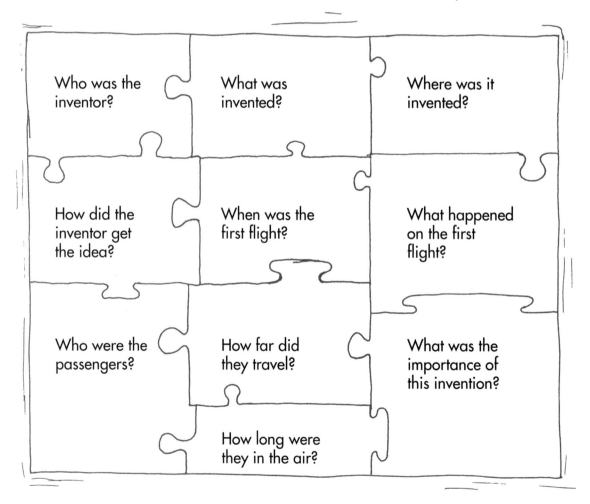

Draw a timeline with the information contained in the puzzle pieces or in the text you read.

PRACTISE SENTENCE AND PARAGRAPH CONSTRUCTION

(LA: Demonstrate an understanding of language conventions and mechanics.)

Rewrite the texts below using capitals, periods, and paragraph indentations where necessary. **Tools E3** and **E4** can help you make your decisions.

travelling by balloon

people have always dreamed of travelling through the skies, over trees, rivers, mountains, and oceans some people built huge balloons to help them travel these balloons looked like enormous flying submarines they were able to transport dozens of passengers at one time these balloons also had a motor that would permit the navigator to steer the balloon that's why these balloons were called dirigibles or airships however, they were also very dangerous hydrogen was used to fill them this is a gas that is easily flammable there were many tragic accidents today, people no longer travel in dirigibles or airships now dirigibles are used to transport heavy cargoes like trees, trucks, and merchandise.

how do planes fly?

an airplane is a flying machine that is heavier than air in order to fly, a plane needs to have wings of a special shape the wings allow the plane to stay up in the air however, before a plane can fly, it needs to be travelling at high speed to allow the wings to lift it into the air the other parts of a plane are the fuselage or main body, the tail and the engine the fuselage is where passengers sit and where cargo is stored the tail of the plane permits the aircraft to stabilize it could be compared to feathers attached to the end of an arrow the tail also contains the rudders which allows the pilot to steer the plane today, the majority of planes have jet-propelled engines the number of passengers wanting to travel by air is constantly increasing, so larger and larger planes are being built the biggest passenger aircraft in the world is the boeing 747 it weighs 367 tonnes and can carry 500 passengers two other giant planes are the douglas dc-10 which can carry up to 400 passengers, as can the L-1011 tri-star.

A
Between Earth and Sky

A.3
Researching Lighter-than-air Craft

RESEARCH A TOPIC IN THE EVOLUTION OF AERONAUTICS

(LA: Develop strategies to analyse media information quickly. Identify/use information gathered from notes to select pertinent details and to organize them logically in the form of a simple research report. Demonstrate an understanding of language conventions and mechanics. Sc: Examine the contributions/impact of science/ technology in societies.)

Here is a list of questions you might like to study. You might use them to do a puzzle like the one on **STEPSpage 18** or you could choose another way of presenting your ideas. See **Tools A8, C4,** and **E3.**

Who were other pioneers of flight?

What other machines were invented or experimented with in the early history of flight? What were they used for?

What are some practical uses for hot air balloons?

Who, in addition to the Montgolfier Brothers, helped perfect the hot air balloon?

What is a glider?
What causes a kite to rise? What causes a glider to rise?

Who invented the first airplane and the first helicopter?
What were the first airplanes and helicopters like?

When did airline companies start regularly scheduled flights?

Why do airplanes come in so many shapes and sizes?

What is the speed of the fastest plane/the slowest plane?

What does the propeller on an airplane do? What is its function?
Why do the engines of jet propelled aircraft make so much noise?

How does a plane take off?

Why is it that satellites launched into space don't fall back to Earth?

How did people get to the moon? How did they get onto the moon?
Are there spaceships that have gone beyond the moon?

Will there be cities in space some day?

Add some questions of your own, remembering to check that each one has a question mark at the end. Look at **Tool A4** for ideas on how to improve the depth of your questions (see open-ended or fat questions).

A

Between
Earth
and Sky

A.3
Researching
Lighter-
than-air
Craft

E.1 PRACTISE SEQUENCING NUMBERS ON A NUMBER LINE

(Ma: Construct/interpret a number line. SS: Represent a series of events on a timeline. Organize a series of events chronologically.)

Read each of the captions below. Draw a timeline and copy the information from each caption onto the timeline at the correct place. **Tool D7** will show you examples of timelines. Abbreviate the dates, speeds, distances, times, and countries when you copy the information. Look in a dictionary for information on abbreviations.

In 1946, the Gloster Meteor clocked a speed record of 990 kilometres per hour.

On October 14, 1947, Chuck Yeager broke the sound barrier in his Bell X-1 jet.

In 1485, Leonardo de Vinci drew a plan for a helicopter.

In 1783, Pilâtre de Rosier travelled 8 kilometres in a hot air balloon.

On December 17, 1903, Wilbur and Orville Wright flew the first motorized airplane in Kitty Hawk in the United States of America. The flight lasted 12 seconds and covered a distance of 40 metres.

In 1985, the Concorde set two new speed records. On February 13, this jet flew from London, England, to Sidney, Australia, in just 17 hours and 3 minutes. On March 28, the Concorde flew from London to South Africa in 8 hours and 8 minutes.

On May 20, 1927, Charles Lindberg flew the first non-stop solo flight across the Atlantic from New York to Paris.

On October 3, 1967, the North American X-15A-2 jet established a speed record never before attained: 7 297 kilometres per hour.

On July 27, 1949, the Comet became the first passenger jet.

Count Zeppelin built his dirigible, the Zeppelin, in 1890.

In 1785, Blanchard and Jefferie succeeded in crossing the English Channel in a hot air balloon.

1100 1150 1200 1250 1300 1350 1400 1450 1500 1550 1600 1650 1700 1750 1800 1850 1900 1950 2000

A

Between Earth and Sky

A.4

Imagine Interviewing a Pioneer of Flight!

(LA: Demonstrate an understanding of interrogative sentences. FA: View a photograph to express an opinion about, and analyse the information it contains.)

Find a picture of a famous pioneer of flight. Looking at the picture, write down the questions you would have liked to ask this person about his or her life and accomplishments (successes). Use **Tool A4** to help you come up with open-ended questions. Be sure to check your questions for punctuation! You might choose to ask one of the inventors in **A.3** "Researching Lighter-than-air Craft", **STEPSpage 21**, about his/her invention.

(LA: Select information and vocabulary according to context, interest, and audience. Select appropriate sources of information. FA: Formulate a dialogue from a given theme. Use appropriate gestures, voice, and special effects.)

With a partner, choose a pioneer of flight whom you would like to know more about. Your task will be to present an oral interview with this pioneer of flight. Together, write down the questions you would like to ask. Then research the answers to these questions, making note of other details that you could use in your interview. Write the answers on cue cards; these will be used by the person who is pretending to be the pioneer of flight in the interview.

In the interview, try to draw out answers to the following questions:
- What were the surroundings like for this person?
- In what period of history did this event occur?
- Where did this interview take place?
- How did this invention affect the lives of the people living at the time of the invention?
- What changes in society would be brought about by this invention?

Tools B1 and **B4** offer ideas on how to put your interview together. Have someone listen to your interview to check that you use the verbs in the correct tense. Even though this pioneer of flight lived in the past, remember that you are pretending to be there interviewing him/her right after the event took place.

Practice the interview several times before presenting it to an audience. You might like to tape the interview on cassette or video or present it "live" before your audience. Think about what costumes would be appropriate. What could you use as a background decor for your interview? **Tool D10** explains how to shoot a simple video, should you decide to tape your interview.

(LA: Select information and vocabulary according to context, interest, and audience. Select appropriate sources of information. FA: Formulate a dialogue from a given theme. Use appropriate gestures, voice, and special effects.)

Interview a pioneer from your community using the same process you used for the above interview. This person might be an inventor, an early resident, someone who has achieved an unusual accomplishment, etc.

(SD: Identify, develop, and sustain means of improving effective expression, as well as effective communication and interaction with other individuals.)

Use **Tool B4** to help you reflect on the outcome of your interview. Record your thoughts in your *Thoughtsteps Journal.* If you used other **Toolbox** cards, complete the corresponding evaluation forms and include them in your *Thoughtsteps Journal.*

Preparing your *Thoughtsteps Journal*

My Game's a Washout!

 Open your *Thoughtsteps Journal*. Add to it a blank page, a lined page, and two more blank pages.
- On the first page, write the title of your theme.
- On the lined page, write the words "Table of Contents". As you work through the theme, list your activities here.
- On the next blank page, list your ideas, words, knowledge relating to temperature, climate, and weather. See **Tool A2**.

 Using your list of ideas from the brainstorming activity, make a poster on the next page of your *Thoughtsteps Journal.* Show words and images about the theme *Discovering Wind and Water*:
My Game's a Washout!

On the back side of this page, write the title "Discovering New Words". As you work through the activities in this theme, list on this page any new words you encounter.

.1 Use a dictionary to review spelling.

Or

E.2 Create a class poster combining everyone's ideas.

Or

E.3 Look through other resource books for ideas for illustrations or words. Add them to your poster.

Or

E.4 Add illustrations to your title page.

Or

E.5 Add a **Bibliography** page. See **Tool A5** to learn how to list your sources.

R Check your poster for spelling. Remember it's a tool you will use during the entire theme! Does it represent the theme? At the bottom of the poster, write down three ideas you would like to explore in this theme.

B

My Game's a Washout!

B.1

Games for Rainy Days

(SD: Identify and develop means of improving acceptance of others' ideas. LA: Identify/use information from appropriate sources to recall and analyse different games.)

Brainstorm a list of activities to do on a rainy day. Refer to **Tools A1** and **A2** to discuss this question:
- What is there to do when it's raining or snowing outside?

As you list your ideas, think about these other questions:
- What do you like about these games or activities?
- How did you start your hobbies or pastimes?
- What do you learn by doing, or playing with, these hobbies, activities, pastimes, games?

(SD: Identify and develop process skills: goal setting, planning, achieving, and evaluating. LA: Identify/use information from appropriate sources to recall and analyse different games and their characteristics. FA: Design a poster for an event. Ma: Use problem-solving strategies to collect and organize data for a survey.)

With the ideas you've collected about rainy day activities, organize a **Rainy Day Games Event** and invite students from other classes to attend.

Start by bringing your games, collections, hobbies to class. In groups of 2 or 3, talk about what you have brought, what this activity means to you, and why you choose to do this activity on a rainy day. As you discuss what you brought, listen for what kind of questions you are asked. See **Tool B1**. Write about your game or activity for a display stand. Use **Tool C8** to help you edit the information you prepare for the event.

Use **Tool A6** to help you plan the details of your **Rainy Day Games Event**. Prepare posters or banners for your event using **Tool D9** for ideas.

During the event, conduct a survey to gather information from the participants. In your survey, ask questions on:
- the grade and age of the visitors;
- their appreciation of the event;
- their preference for a particular display;
- their desire to participate in another event like this one.

E.1 (Ma: Construct and interpret graphs to represent data collected from surveys.)
Make a graph of the results of your survey. Use **Tools D4** and **D5** to help make your graph.

Or

E.2 (FA: Demonstrate an understanding of written musical symbols. Translate written symbols into music. Create an original selection of music. Using instruments, produce variations in intensity.)
Examine the exchange game "At the Flea Market" on **STEPSpage 26**. The participants in this game first explore how musical notes vary in length, then simulate a rainstorm using musical notes/instruments. The rainstorm could be recorded and then played as part of the advertising for the **Rainy Day Games Event** or at the opening of the event.

(SD: Identify and develop means of improving relationships and interactions with others.)
In your *Thoughtsteps Journal*, evaluate your survey to decide what about this type
of event you would do again and what changes you might make. Note these ideas.
Take time to reflect on your own participation in this event and what you learned
about a new game or hobby that interests you; how different ages might be
attracted to different types of games. **Tool A9** could give you some ideas to reflect
on.

If you used other **Toolbox** cards, complete the corresponding evaluation forms and
include them in your *Thoughtsteps Journal*.

B

My Game's
a Washout!

B.1

*Games
for
Rainy Days*

B

My Game's a Washout!

B.1

Games for Rainy Days

E.2 (FA: Demonstrate an understanding of written musical symbols. Translate written symbols into music. Create an original selection of music. Using instruments, produce variations in intensity.)

(Part 1): This exchange game is called "At the Flea Market". It will help you explore how musical notes vary in length. It is best played with a larger group of students. After you have finished the first part of the game, you will work on creating a rainstorm using instruments and notes of varying lengths.

Using the chart below, create a series of 240 musical note trading cards for exchanging in the class (see **Tool E1**):

NUMBER OF CARDS	NOTES	LENGTH	PAUSE INDICATORS
8	whole note	4 counts	full rest
16	half note	2 counts	half rest
32	quarter	1 count	quarter rest
64	eighth	1/2 count	eighth rest

Each team of 2 players chooses enough cards to equal 16 counts
(e.g., 1 whole note = 4 counts, 2 half-notes = 4 counts,
3 quarter notes = 3 counts and 2 eighth notes = 1 count).

The leader of the game strikes a note on the triangle or the piano and announces the number of counts to be exchanged. The teams then have 30 seconds to exchange their cards and recount them to be sure they still have 16 counts before the leader rings again. After having completed several exchanges, each team writes their last set of notes on the board or on a chart in sequence.

Divide the class into four groups and give each group a different type of percussion instrument. (This exercise may also be done with body percussions or vocal sounds instead of instruments.)

Group 1 plays whole notes using a metal instrument (e.g., triangles, cymbals).
Group 2 plays half notes using an instrument with keys (e.g., xylophone, piano).
Group 3 plays quarter notes with drums or sticks.
Group 4 plays eighth notes with wind instruments (e.g., flute).

As the leader counts and points to the notes on the board or on the chart, the musicians play the notes. (The leader could also write either the symbol for crescendo (<) or decrescendo (>) above the note patterns and have the groups play the notes with increasing or decreasing volume. These symbols can be compared with the math symbols < and > to discuss their similarities/differences.)

E.2 **(Part 2):** Now, using the same groups, recreate a thunder shower at the flea market. See **Tool B3.**

Group 2 plays alone for 16 counts and continues to play to the end.
Group 3 joins in after 16 counts and plays for 48 counts.
Group 4 joins in after 32 counts and plays for 32 counts.
Group 1 joins in after 48 counts for 16 counts or 4 thunderclaps.
Group 4 stops playing 16 counts after the thunder **(group 1)**.
Group 3 stops playing 16 counts after **group 4**.
Group 2 stops playing 16 counts after the **group 3**.

Discuss how the volume and texture in this exercise create an emotional impact. Why does a rainstorm have a soft-loud-soft (< >) shape to its sound? How does this crescendo-decrescendo create an emotional impact? Complete the evaluation form from **Tool B3.**

B

My Game's
a Washout!

B.1
Games
for
Rainy Days

B

My Game's
a Washout!

B.2

*Ways of
Adapting
to the
Weather*

(LA: Identify/use information to establish cause/effect relationships in a debate.)
Discuss the pros and cons of having hot, sunny weather all the time.
Debate the following statement:

> *"Everyone would be much happier if the weather was always
> hot and sunny."*

Form a group of four students. Follow the rules of debating outlined in **Tool B5**.
Before you begin your work together, examine **Tools A1** and **A7**. At the end
of your debate, evaluate your performance as a member of the group.

(LA: Identify/use information gathered from notes and appropriate sources for a simple research report.
Organize ideas logically. Demonstrate an understanding of language conventions and mechanics. Sc: Examine
the contributions/impact of science/technology in societies.)
Research how people adapt, through inventions, to their environment and to
different types of weather. Choose one of the following climates to explore: hot
and sunny, rainy, windy, snowy, foggy, stormy, cold (icy). Brainstorm the inventions
humans have created to adapt to this climate. Use **Tool A2** to help you. You may
need to locate other resources to find more inventions. See **Tool A5**.
From your list, choose a maximum of five inventions and research how they work
and how they enable people to adapt to their environment. **STEPSpage 30** has
a list of some inventions to get you started. These are inventions that you are
accustomed to seeing. Explore the inventions used by people in other cultures to
adapt to life in the desert, along the coast, in the alpine regions, in polar climates.

Use **Tools A8, C4** and **C8** to complete your research project. If this is a group
project, review **Tool A7** and choose your focus for this project.

E.1 (SS: Understand how humans adapt to their environment through their inventions. Sc: Understand the
relationships between living organisms and their environment with respect to climate.)
Construct a pair of Inuit sunglasses. See **STEPSpage 31** and **Tool C7**.

Or

E.2 (SS: Understand how humans adapt to their environment through their inventions. Sc: Understand the
relationships between living organisms and their environment with respect to climate.)
Design the right clothing for summer or winter wear. See **STEPSpage 32**
and **Tool C7**.

Or

E.3 (Sc: Understand the relationships between living organisms and their environment with respect to
climate.)
Experiment to demonstrate how weather affects the behaviour of living
things. See **STEPSpage 33** for a description of the experiment.

Or

E.4 (FA: In a drawing, represent people interacting with certain facets of the environment. LA: Identify/use information from a text to extrapolate and establish relationships for an imaginary story. Demonstrate an understanding of language conventions and mechanics.)

Illustrate the facial expressions of two people who mixed up their plane tickets and who have just "deplaned" in a climate opposite to the one they expected to arrive in. See **Tools A1, C2,** and **C8**.

Example: You live in the Bahamas and you're on your way to Barbados. As you head to your departure gate you bump into another traveller and you both drop your tickets. You pick up your ticket and hurry onto your plane, only to find out that you're on a plane headed for Iqualuit in northern Canada. You're wearing sandals, shorts and a flowery print shirt. What will you do? How do you think the other passenger will feel getting off in Barbados?

Write a story about these two people.

R (SD: Identify and develop means of improving understanding of cause/effect relationships.)

In your *Thoughtsteps Journal*, reflect on your participation within a group by using **Tool A7** or, if this was an individual project, use **Tools C4** and **A8**.

INVENTIONS FOR ALL KINDS OF WEATHER

(LA: Identify/use information gathered from notes and appropriate sources for a simple research report. Organize ideas logically. Demonstrate an understanding of language conventions and mechanics. Sc: Examine the contributions/impact of science/technology in societies.)

Use these ideas to start thinking about your research project. See **Tool C4**. Write a list of words that describe each invention (adjectives) to use in your explanation.

INVENTIONS FOR HOT, SUNNY WEATHER:	ADJECTIVES THAT DESCRIBE:
parasol	large, curved, etc.
sunscreen	creamy, white, etc.
sunglasses, visor	
air conditioning, fans	
swimwear, shorts	
INVENTIONS FOR RAINY WEATHER:	
gumboots	rubber, glossy, lined, etc.
umbrella	
windshield wipers	
gutters	
mudflaps on cars	
INVENTIONS FOR WINDY WEATHER:	
windbreaker	nylon, resistant, etc.
windmill	
lightning-rod	
aerodynamic cars	
sailboats	
INVENTIONS FOR ICE:	
antifreeze	liquid, blue, etc.
icebreaker ships	
road sanders	
skates	
car door-lock de-icers	
INVENTIONS FOR FOG:	
foghorn	loud, booming, etc.
lighthouses	
radar	
foglights	
line markers in the pavement and at the sides of the road	
INVENTIONS FOR SNOW:	
snowtires	deep treads, durable, etc.
snowploughs and snow shovels	
ski-doos	
down-filled jackets	
mittens, scarves	

ℰ.1 CONSTRUCT A PAIR OF INUIT SUNGLASSES

(SS: Understand how humans adapt to their environment through their inventions. Sc: Understand the relationships between living organisms and their environment with respect to climate.)

In the far north, Inuit people learned long ago that it is necessary to protect the eyes from too much exposure to the sunlight reflected from the snow. They invented sunglasses made out of caribou or seal bones.

Here's how you can make a simple version of Inuit sunglasses:

MATERIALS REQUIRED:

• an egg carton	• paint
• a pair of scissors	• string
• decorations for your glasses	• glue

PROCEDURE:

1. Cut a strip of two eggwells from your egg carton.
2. Cut a fine slit across the bottom of each egg well. Trim a triangle from the joining strip of the egg carton so that the "glasses" will fit over your nose.
3. Thread your string through a small hole at the top corners of your glasses.
4. Decorate your sunglasses with paint and other objects: stickers, glitter, etc.
5. Try wearing your glasses outside on a sunny day. Do they work well? Do you think they protect your eyes? Why?
6. Can you think of another way that the Inuit could have protected their eyes in the past? Write your comments on this project in your *Thoughtsteps Journal.* Evaluate this activity using **Tool C7.**

B

My Game's
a Washout!

B.2

*Ways of
Adapting
to the
Weather*

E.2 WHAT COLOUR SHOULD I WEAR?

(SS: Understand how humans adapt to their environment through their inventions. Sc: Understand the relationships between living organisms and their environment with respect to climate.)

Have you ever wondered what clothing to wear on a hot summer's day? How could you dress to stay cool? What colour clothing do you think would be best to wear on a hot day? Write your hypothesis down before you try this experiment. Use the format in **Tool C5.**

MATERIALS REQUIRED:

- a sheet of black paper
- a sheet of white paper
- adhesive tape
- an outside thermometer
- two thermometers

PROCEDURE:

1. Using adhesive tape, attach a thermometer to the centre of each sheet of paper. If necessary, hang the outside thermometer.
2. Record the temperature shown on each of the two thermometers as well as the temperature on the thermometer outside.
3. Place the two sheets of paper on a window ledge in the sun so that the thermometers are underneath the papers.
4. Leave the papers in the sun for at least one hour. Check the temperature on each thermometer at the end of this time.

OBSERVATIONS:
What differences did you notice?
Were the temperatures the same?

CONCLUSION:
Which paper absorbed the most heat? How does this compare to your hypothesis? What colours of clothing would you be better off wearing in the summer heat? Why?

> Now that you know more about colours and clothing, imagine yourself as a fashion designer. Could you come up with a new style of clothing for the summer? Illustrate your designs in colour of course!

E.3 FLY IN SLOW MOTION

(Sc: Understand the relationships between living organisms and their environment with respect to climate.)

Weather affects the behaviour of living things. Heat, humidity (moisture in the air), and stormy weather can destroy sources of food and threaten the survival of certain species.

Cold-blooded animals like snakes are very sensitive to changes in temperature. This experiment will allow you to observe how temperature affects a cold-blooded animal, in this case, the household fly.

Use the format in **Tool C5.**

MATERIALS REQUIRED:

• a fly	• a nail
• a jar with a lid	• a piece of scrap wood
• a hammer	• a refrigerator

PROCEDURE:

1. Place your lid on the piece of scrap wood. Using the hammer and nail, pierce several holes in the lid so that your fly will be able to breathe.
2. Place the fly in the jar and close the lid.
3. Place the jar in the refrigerator. After 30 minutes, remove the jar and observe the fly's actions.
   - How does the fly behave?
   - Does it fly slower or faster than before?
   Record your observations.
4. Be sure to let the fly go as soon as you have completed your experiment.

(LA: Identify/use information from images to establish relationships. Demonstrate an understanding of adjectives.)

Observe the sky twice a day for five days and then, in your *Thoughtsteps Journal*, draw the different cloud formations that you see. Also, describe what the weather is like each day. Use an information chart like the one that has been started here.

		CHARTING CLOUD FORMATIONS AND THE WEATHER:	
DATE	**TIME**	**ILLUSTRATION OF CLOUD FORMATION**	**DESCRIPTION OF WEATHER**

Use the explanations on cloud formations on **STEPSpage 36** to label your illustrations. Is it possible to predict the weather by looking at cloud formations?

Make a list of some adjectives that might be used to describe clouds. Write other lists of adjectives that might be used to describe rain, snow, wind, or sunshine. See **Tool E2** for a definition of the term adjective and **Tools A3** and **D1** for help with your viewing and representing skills.

(LA: Identify/use information from appropriate sources to summarize weather predictions on a chart. Sc: Examine the contributions/impact of science/technology in societies.)

Read "My Baseball Game's a Washout!", **pages 19** to **23** of your text *Discovering Wind and Water* to learn about alternative ways to predict the weather. Discuss the following questions with a group.
- How scientific do you think these methods are? Explain.
- In your opinion, which method is the most reliable? Why?
- Do you think meteorologists still observe groundhogs or kelp to predict the weather? Why? Consult the illustrations on **page 23** of *Discovering Wind and Water* to support your answer.
- Do you think it's better to observe cloud formations or to observe the colour of the sky to predict the weather? Explain.

After reading this selection and discussing the questions above, interview your parents, grandparents, or a person in your community to learn about the methods they use for predicting the weather. See **Tool C4**. Write a short explanation of their methods, remembering to use adjectives to be as precise as possible about the type of weather being predicted and the methods used to predict it. Present your findings to the class.

The different explanations could be posted in a chart format with the headings: **Predicting rain, sunshine, snow, wind,** etc. See **Tool A3**.

**.1** (Sc: Use the scientific process to understand how clouds are formed.)
Experiment by following the directions on **STEPSpage 37** and **Tool C5**.

Or

.2-3 (Sc: Use the scientific process to understand how wind and rain are formed.)
Experiment by following the directions on **STEPSpages 38** and **39** and **Tool C5**.

(SD: Understand the importance of change as a means of growth as an individual.)
What did you learn? What would you still like to know about predicting the weather? Using the results from your research and **Tool C4**, complete a PMI chart (see **Tool A3**) to reflect on what you know now about the weather. In your PMI chart, list your most interesting (Plus) and least interesting discoveries (Minus), as well as the questions or ideas you would still like to investigate (Importance undecided).

If you used other **Toolbox** cards, complete the corresponding evaluation forms and include them in your *Thoughtsteps Journal*.

B
My Game's a Washout!

B.3
My Baseball Game's a Washout!

B

My Game's
a Washout!

B.3

*My Baseball
Game's
a Washout!*

CLOUD FORMATIONS

(LA: Identify/use information from images to establish relationships.)

Here is a list of the most common cloud formations. You won't be able to observe them all at any one time though.

CIRRUS:

These high clouds indicate a change in the weather is on its way.

ALTOSTRATUS:

These slender, grey bands of clouds appear high in the sky. Later on, these grey bands might form rain or snow clouds.

CUMULONIMBUS:

These thick, towering clouds form huge columns in the sky. They bring with them hail, rain, or snow.

CUMULUS:

These are the little isolated clouds that can be seen dotted across the sky on a sunny day.

STRATUS:

These low clouds bring with them light rain. Stratus clouds may also form fog at low altitudes near water.

STEPS TO DISCOVERING...   ...WIND AND WATER

.1 EXPERIMENT WITH CLOUD FORMATION

(Sc: Use the scientific process to understand how clouds are formed.)

Clouds are formed as hot air rises and comes in contact with cooler air. The hot air contains water vapour (that's water in the form of a gas). When the vapour is cooled, it condenses (or comes back together) to form millions of tiny water droplets. Here is an experiment to observe the process of condensation:

Use **Tool C5** to help you write your experiment.

MATERIALS REQUIRED:
- hot water
- an ice cube
- a sheet of black paper
- a glass pop bottle (or other bottle with a narrow opening)

PROCEDURE:
1. Fill the bottle with hot water. Let it sit for a minute. Then pour 3/4 of the water from the bottle into another container.
2. Place the ice cube over the opening in the bottle.
3. Fold the sheet of black paper and place it like a screen behind the bottle so you can observe what is happening inside the bottle.

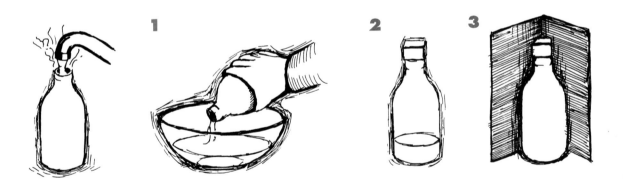

OBSERVATIONS:
Record your observations on the hot air rising from the water. What happens to the air when it meets the cold air from the ice cube?

B

My Game's
a Washout!

B.3

My Baseball
Game's
a Washout!

E.2 EXPERIMENT WITH WIND FORMATION

(Sc: Use the scientific process to understand how wind is formed.)

Do you know how wind is created? Write your hypothesis or theory down in your journal before you start this experiment. Use **Tool C5** to help you write your experiment.

MATERIALS REQUIRED:

- hot and cold water
- a piece of cardboard
- two identical glass bottles or jars
- blue, red, or green food colouring
- a towel

PROCEDURE:

1. Pour hot water mixed with several drops of food colouring into the first bottle. Place this bottle on a towel.
2. Fill the second bottle to the brim with cold water.
3. Place the piece of cardboard over the opening of the cold water bottle. Holding the cardboard firmly in place, inverse this bottle over the first one and carefully remove the cardboard.

OBSERVATIONS:

What happens to the hot water when it meets the cold water?

CONCLUSION:

If the water was air, what do you think would happen? Can you think of another experiment to show how wind is created? Try it at home before presenting your experiment to the class.

E.3 EXPERIMENT WITH RAIN FORMATION

(Sc: Use the scientific process to understand how rain is formed.)

How do you think rain forms? Write down your hypothesis before trying this experiment. Use **Tool C5** to help you write your experiment.

MATERIALS REQUIRED:

- an electric kettle
- an ice cube
- a tablespoon

PROCEDURE:

1. Fill the kettle with water and bring it to a boil. Unplug the kettle.
2. Place an ice cube on the spoon and hold it over the steam.

OBSERVATIONS:

What happens to the steam? What happens to the bottom of the spoon? Where do the water droplets come from?

CONCLUSION:

After completing this experiment, can you describe how rain is formed? Does this agree with your hypothesis? Can you think of another experiment to show how rain forms? Try your ideas at home before presenting your new experiment in class.

1

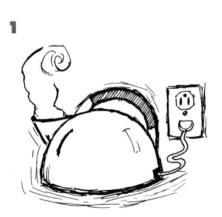

2

B

My Game's a Washout!

B.4

A Home-Made Weather Station

(LA: Identify/use information from a text/images to select and reproduce pertinent details. Demonstrate an understanding of the use of the apostrophe.)

Watch a televised weather report to learn how meteorologists describe the weather. List the terms used during the report: partly sunny, overcast, atmospheric pressure, visibility, wind factor, precipitation and temperature, etc. To check your listening skills, see **Tool B1**.

After watching the weather report on television, read a weather bulletin in a newspaper or the report described on **STEPSpage 42.** Answer the questions on **STEPSpage 43** as you read this report. To check your use of an apostrophe (see **Tool E4**), complete the weather report on **STEPSpage 44.**

Follow the process described in **Tool A1** to answer the following questions.
- How would you go about writing a weather report?
- What instruments would you need to build or locate to be able to write your own forecast?
- How do you think meteorologists collect information for the weather reports? What instruments do they use?

(LA: Identify/use information from a text to gather meanings, experiment, and make decisions. Sc: Construct, use, and study tools which measure changes in climate and temperature. Ma: Use problem-solving strategies to collect data. Select/construct/interpret appropriate graphs, charts, lists, and tables to represent the data collected. Use metric units and instruments to measure data.)

To construct a weather station with a barometer (air and water), rain gauge, weathervane, anemometer and/or a meteorological instrument shelter, follow the directions given on **pages 24** to **31** of *Discovering Wind and Water*. You will probably want to work in a team of 3-4 students. (See **Tool C7** to examine how well you follow directions.) Once you have constructed your weather instrument, explain to others what your instrument measures and how it works. Compare your instruments with those shown on **page 23** of *Discovering Wind and Water*.

Place your instruments outside. Collect data twice a day for at least 5 days and record the results, using a chart like the one below. From your chart, write a weather forecast that can be posted at the entrance to your school for students to consult at recess or at lunch.

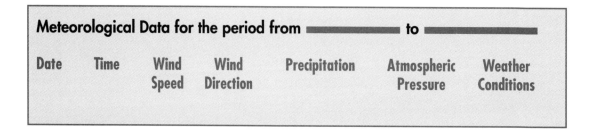

Meteorological Data for the period from ▬▬▬▬ to ▬▬▬▬						
Date	Time	Wind Speed	Wind Direction	Precipitation	Atmospheric Pressure	Weather Conditions

Compare the data you collect each day with the predictions in the newspaper and on television. Post the newspaper clippings beside your recorded information. See **Tool D6** to evaluate your chart. Create graphs to represent your results. See **Tool D5**.

B

My Game's
a Washout!

B.4
A
Home-Made
Weather
Station

E.1 (Sc: Understand weather-related phenomena. SS: Understand that human activity affects the environment.)

Research other weather-related phenomena. See **STEPSpage 45** and **Tool C4**.

Or

E.2 (Ma: Represent data collected, for temperature and precipitation, on a climate graph.)

Record temperarure and precipitation on a climate graph. See **STEPSpage 46** and **Tool D5**.

Or

E.3 (Sc: Construct, use, and study tools which measure changes in climate and temperature.)

Research the instruments meteorologists use to predict the weather. Compare the purposes of these instruments with the ones you constructed. See **Tool C4** and **page 23** of *Discovering Wind and Water*.

(Sc: Construct, use, and study tools which measure changes in climate and temperature. SD: Identify and develop process skills: goal setting, planning, achieving, and evaluating.)

Using the data you collected and the newspaper clippings on the weather for the days you observed, answer the questions on **STEPSpage 47**. Write your answers in your *Thoughtsteps Journal*.

If you used other **Toolbox** cards, complete the corresponding evaluation forms and include them in your *Thoughtsteps Journal*.

B
My Game's a Washout!

B.4
A Home-Made Weather Station

READ A SAMPLE WEATHER BULLETIN
AND LEARN THE SYMBOLS USED
(LA: Identify/use information from a text/images to select and reproduce pertinent details.)

Use the information from the weather bulletin below to answer the questions on **STEPSpage 43**.

SUNDAY, AUGUST 29, VANCOUVER, B.C.
The weather outlook for today and tomorrow:

TODAY
partly sunny
maximum 21°C

THIS EVENING
partly covered skies
minimum 12°C

TOMORROW
sunny with cloudy periods
maximum 22°C, minimum 13°C

Sunrise at 6:25 a.m.   Moon appears at 6:35 p.m.
Sunset at 8:02 p.m.   Moon disappears at 4:01 a.m.

TEMPERATURES TODAY:

in the major Canadian cities	in the major U.S. cities	in the major urban centres in British Columbia
Calgary 14/6	Boston 35/25	Abbotsford 23/9
Charlottetown 22/11	Chicago 25/19	Comox 21/12
Dawson City 15/4	Dallas 34/23	Cranbrook 14/6
Edmonton 16/6	Denver 29/13	Kamloops 20/13
Fredericton 24/12	Honolulu 32/22	Kelowna 21/8
Halifax 23/11	Las Vegas 36/24	Nanaimo 20/12
London 27/16	Maui 34/22	Penticton 16/9
Moncton 23/11	Miami 33/25	Prince George 14/3
Montréal 23/12	New York 36/26	Prince Rupert 16/10
Ottawa 23/12	Phoenix 36/23	Terrace 20/11
Québec 24/11	Portland 23/12	Victoria 23/10
Regina 17/7	Reno 34/11	
Saint John's 20/11	Salt Lake City 32/12	
Sault St.Marie 24/14	San Fransisco 31/15	
Saskatoon 16/4	Seattle 22/13	
Sudbury 24/12	Washington 35/24	
Timmins 23/12		
Toronto 25/15		
Whitehorse 14/4		
Windsor 28/18		
Winnipeg 19/11		
Yellowknife 13/6		

PRECIPITATION IN VANCOUVER:

Today:	0 mm
For the month to date:	19.0 mm
Since January:	583.4 mm
Compared with this time last year:	669.9 mm

LEARN TO READ A WEATHER BULLETIN

(LA: Identify/use information from a text/images to select and reproduce pertinent details.)

As you read the information on **STEPSpage 42** (or from other newspaper clippings of weather reports), answer the following questions:

What information can you collect from a weather report?

1. On Sunday, August 29, the maximum temperature forecast, in degrees Celsius, for the city of Vancouver was ▬▬▬.

2. The day was ▬▬▬ hr. ▬▬▬ min. long.

3. The skies in the Vancouver region were ▬▬▬▬▬▬▬.

4. The moon rose at ▬▬▬.

5. It was coldest in the city of ▬▬▬▬▬▬▬▬.

6. It was warmest in the city of ▬▬▬▬▬▬▬▬.

7. The average temperature in British Columbia that day was ▬▬▬.

8. Why are two temperatures shown for each city?▬▬▬▬▬.

9. Vancouver's total precipitation for this day was ▬▬▬.

10. Vancouver's total annual precipitation to this date was ▬▬▬.

11. What symbols are used to represent:

temperature?   snow?

rain?   snow mixed with rain?

clear skies?   sun mixed with rain?

fog?   overcast skies?

wind direction?   partly sunny skies?

storms?

Complete **Tool D1** to analyse your viewing skills.

LEARN TO USE AN APOSTROPHE

(LA: Demonstrate an understanding of the use of the apostrophe.)

Can you change the written weather report below to make it sound like you were reading it aloud? In speaking, we often take shortcuts by cutting out letters or syllables and replacing them with an apostrophe. "I would recommend" might become "I'd recommend...". Can you explain what the other apostrophes in the text are used to represent? See **Tool E4**.

Here is the Thursday evening weather forecast. Today's weather was partly sunny with a high of 21 degrees Celsius. It is going to be a partly cloudy sky tonight. We will be seeing the sun again tomorrow though there will be some intermittent clouds. You will still be able to enjoy a walk outside, but I would suggest you take a sweater with you.

The sun will be up at 6:25 a.m. tomorrow morning. It will set at 8:02 p.m. tomorrow evening. How is that for precise timing?! The moon will appear at 6:35 p.m. and set at 4:01 a.m. Do not try to stay up all night just to see the moon go down!

So there you have it ladies and gentlemen! It looks like it should not be a bad day tomorrow. Be sure to get out and enjoy it for, as you are aware, winter is on its way, and there will be lots of time to sit inside then.

Speaking of winter… you do not know how lucky you are to be living here. We have just heard from our weather forecast station in St.John's, Newfoundland, where they are calling for hurricane force winds and snow storms. If you have relatives in that part of the country, you may have difficulty reaching them in the next few days. The storm is likely to pull down a few telephone and power lines. I know it is not polite to wish bad luck on someone else, but I am quite happy that it is their turn to have the storm. We have just finished a long period of fog and overcast skies and I am not ready for more bad weather just yet.

This is the end of tonight's report. Thank you for listening and tune in again tomorrow night.

𝓔.1 RESEARCH OTHER WEATHER-RELATED PHENOMENA

(Sc: Understand weather-related phenomena. Understand that human activity affects the environment.)

The weather plays an important role in our everyday lives. Measuring and recording the weather is just one aspect of meteorology. Studying how weather relates to the problems and disasters that we face is another interesting aspect of meteorology. Here are a few topics that you might like to study in greater detail. Use **Tool C4** to help you plan and organize your research topic. **Tool A8** will give you ideas on how you might present your information.

The greenhouse effect

The ozone layer

Acid rain and smog

Hurricanes

Cyclones and tornadoes

Aurora borealis: the northern lights

The disappearing rainforests

Hydroelectric power dams and reservoirs

Advantages and disadvantages of irrigation

Artificial cloud insemination: creating rain clouds

Volcanic eruptions and their effect on the weather

Satellites and their information: e.g., RADARSAT

First Peoples and their knowledge of weather

Drought

Tropical monsoons

El Niño

Floods

Blizzards and sandstorms

B

My Game's
a Washout!

B.4

**A
Home-Made
Weather
Station**

.2 RECORD TEMPERATURE AND PRECIPITATION ON A CLIMATE GRAPH

(Ma: Represent data collected, for temperature and precipitation, on a climate graph.)

Once you have gathered your information from your weather station, you might like to graph the results. A climate graph is an excellent way to record both temperature and precipitation. See **Tool D5** for other types of graphs and how to construct them.

Here is how to record your information:

Record the average temperatures by making a dot where the temperature reading meets the middle of the bar for each day. Once you have marked the temperatures for each day, connect the dots with a red pen to make your line graph.

To record the precipitation, simply colour in the bar to the number of mm of rain or snow that fell for each day with a blue pen or pencil crayon.

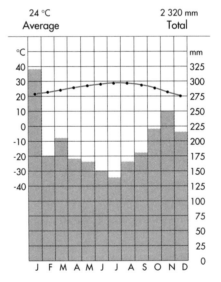

Period of time (e.g., dates or months)

1. What was the average temperature for the period of time you kept your records? Add the temperatures for each day together and then divide by the number of days in the study.

2. What was the average precipitation for this same period?

3. What was the range in temperature? Subtract the lowest temperature from the highest temperature. The difference will be the range in temperature for the period you recorded.

4. What was the range in precipitation for this same period?

ANSWER THE REFLECTION QUESTIONS ON METEOROLOGY

(Sc: Construct, use, and study tools which measure changes in the climate and temperature. Identify and develop process skills: goal setting, planning, achieving, and evaluating.)

B

My Game's a Washout!

B.4

A Home-Made Weather Station

Using the data you collected from your weather station, the newspaper clippings on the weather for the days you observed, and the information from *Discovering Wind and Water*, answer the questions below. Record your answers in your *Thoughtsteps Journal*.

1. What cloud formations did you observe? Did they help you predict the weather for the following day? Was the chart on cloud formations useful to you in your task?

2. What was the temperature when the atmospheric pressure was low/high? Did your instruments accurately reflect the temperature and air pressure?

3. What cloud formations were visible when the atmospheric pressure was low/high? How are cloud formations and atmospheric pressure related?

4. What cloud formations were visible when the wind was blowing from the north in a southerly direction/from the east/from the west/from the south? Was there a pattern?

5. What was the wind speed when the weather was warm/cool? Was there a pattern?

6. From what direction was the wind blowing when it was warm/cool? Was there a pattern?

7. What cloud formations were visible when it was warm/cool/rainy/foggy, etc.? Was there a pattern?

8. What comments would you like to make about how your group worked together to set goals, plan the project, carry it out, and then to evaluate it? Do you have suggestions for improving your process skills the next time you work on a project?

You might want to add other questions and/or answers to your *Thoughtsteps Journal*. What else did you discover in working with your weather station? Use **Tool A9** to summarize your learning experience with this activity.

B

My Game's a Washout!

B.5

The Muscles of the Sun and Wind

(LA: Identify/use appropriate sources of information to experiment or validate the message. Sc: Use the scientific process to study different forms of energy production and uses.)

Experiment with how the sun and the wind can be used for energy. Find a partner and choose one of the experiments described on **STEPSpage 50** and **51**. Use the format described in **Tool C5**.

(Sc: Examine the contributions/impact of science/technology in societies. Recognize that humans have the power to make choices to conserve and protect the environment. FA: Create a mural representing interactions between living and non-living elements in the environment. LA: Identify/use information from an image to identify characteristics and evaluate relationships or question the premises for them.)

Create a mural showing the possible uses of sun and wind as energy. See **Tool D3**.

Before you start working on this project, find at least three partners and several reference books on energy and machines or instruments used to harness these energy forms. See **Tool A5**. Consult the illustrations, "The Sun and Wind at Work", shown on **pages 32** and **33** of *Discovering Wind and Water*. Divide the mural into four parts using four sheets of equal sized paper that can later be glued or stapled against a larger background of a different colour. Decide which of the four themes you would like to develop for the mural:
- sun (or wind) as a form of energy for everyday use,

OR

- sun (or wind) as a replacement form for today's energy sources.

Using newspaper clippings, magazine pictures, illustrations, etc., complete your part of the mural with as many colourful and detailed examples as possible.

Present your part of the mural to the other three partners or to the remainder of the class. In your presentation you might explore the following questions:
- How could this source of energy replace a non-renewable energy source in use today?
- How could this source of energy be made more popular or more widely available?
- What are the advantages and/or disadvantages of this form of energy?

E.1 (Sc: Study different forms of energy production and uses.)

Using the reference materials at your disposal, and **Tool C4**, explore other weather related forms of energy with respect to the ideas on **STEPSpage 52**.

E.2 (FA: Use instruments to reproduce variations in the parameters of sounds. With predetermined criteria, explore different means of producing sound. Sc: Explore ways of transmitting sound. Understand that variations in pitch and intensity are a result of speed and density.)

Explore how "wind" is used to make musical sounds in wind instruments or home-made instruments like chimes, tubes, pipes, etc.
- Why do several bottles filled with water to varying levels produce different pitches of sound when you blow across the top?
- How do musicians change the pitch of sound on wind instruments like the flute, the oboe, the clarinet?
- How many different sounds can you create with wind? Can you record them?
- Explore how the wind speed or the density of an object affect the pitch and intensity of the sounds produced.

R (SD: Identify and develop process skills: goal setting, planning, achieving, and evaluating.)
Using **Tool A9**, reflect on how you worked as a member of a group to complete your mural project. What difficulties did you encounter and how did you overcome them?

If you used other **Toolbox** cards, complete the corresponding evaluation forms and include them in your *Thoughtsteps Journal*.

B

My Game's
a Washout!

B.5

*The Muscles
of the Sun
and Wind*

EXPERIMENT WITH HOW THE SUN AND THE WIND
CAN BE USED FOR ENERGY

(LA: Identify/use appropriate sources of information to experiment or validate the message. Sc: Use the scientific process to study different forms of energy production and uses.)

Find a partner and choose one of the experiments described below. Use the format described in **Tool C5** to complete the experiment of your choice.

Using Solar Energy to ☆ur Advantage

MATERIALS REQUIRED:

• 2 glasses	• 1 sheet of black paper
• adhesive tape	• 1 sheet of white paper
• a thermometer to place outside	• two thermometers

PROCEDURE:

1. Cover the sides of one glass with black paper and the sides of the other glass with white paper. Use tape to hold the paper in place.
2. Fill each glass with water, leaving 1 cm at the top.
3. Place the two glasses on a window sill in the sun. Record the temperature outside. Place a thermometer in each glass. Record the temperature of the water in each glass after one minute.
4. Leave the glasses in the sun for at least one hour. Record the temperature of the water in each glass at that time.

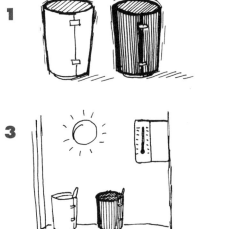

OBSERVATIONS:

Are the temperatures in the two glasses the same? Which glass contains warmer water?

CONCLUSION:

How could you use the energy generated by the sun?

Using Wind Energy to Our Advantage

MATERIALS REQUIRED:

- a pencil and scissors
- adhesive tape
- 1 sheet of construction paper 15 cm x 15 cm
- a thumbtack and a small stick (a chopstick will do)

PROCEDURE:

1. Draw diagonal lines between the corners of your square paper. Mark a point halfway between the centre of the square and the corner.
2. Cut along each line from the corner to the marked point.
3. Fold the right side of each cut into the centre and use adhesive tape to hold the folded points together.
4. Push the thumbtack into the centre of your pinwheel and then into the stick, checking to be sure that the pinwheel turns easily.

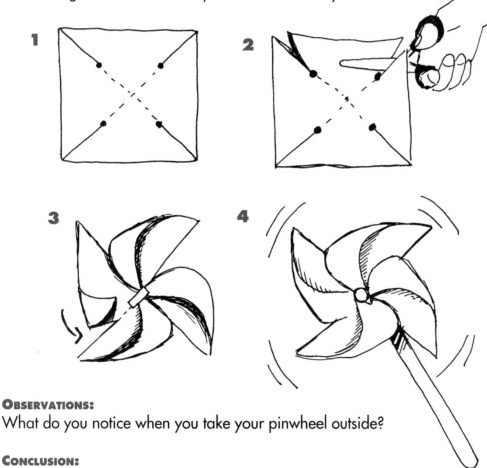

OBSERVATIONS:

What do you notice when you take your pinwheel outside?

CONCLUSION:

How could you use the energy generated by the wind? How could your pinwheel be adapted to function on a bigger scale?

B

My Game's
a Washout!

B.5
The Muscles
of the Sun
and Wind

E.1 EXPLORE OTHER FORMS OF ENERGY

(Sc: Study different forms of energy production and uses.)

The following mind map will start you thinking about the sun and other forms of energy and how they relate. Use **Tool A3** for more information or mind maps.

Begin by thinking about this idea:

> "The sun is the most important source of energy for our planet. Without the sun, no other form of energy could exist. Here is how the sun influences other sources of energy."

Then complete the mind map below by drawing arrows to describe the relationship between the sun and other energy forms.

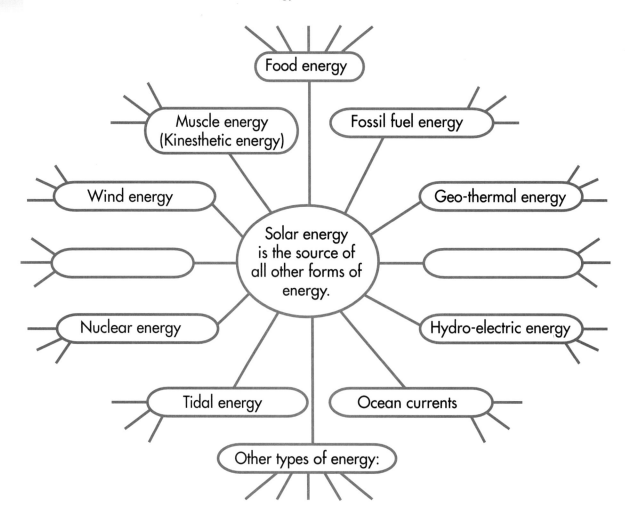

Preparing your *Thoughtsteps Journal*

C

Tales Told by Water

Open your *Thoughtsteps Journal*. Add to it a blank page, a lined page, and two more blank pages.
- On the first page, write the title of your theme.
- On the lined page, write the words "Table of Contents". As you work through the them, list your activities here.
- On the next blank page, list your ideas, words, knowledge relating to water, uses of water, its cycle, and electricity using water. See **Tool A2**.

Using your list of words from the brainstorming activity, make a poster on the next page of your *Thoughtsteps Journal*. Show words and images about the theme *Discovering Wind and Water*: **Tales Told by Water**.

On the back side of this page, write the title "Discovering New Words". As you work through the activities in this theme, list on this page any new words you encounter.

E.1 Use a dictionary to review spelling.

Or

E.2 Create a class poster combining everyone's ideas.

Or

E.3 Look through other resource books for ideas for illustrations or words. Add them to your poster.

Or

E.4 Add illustrations to your title page.

Or

E.5 Add a **Bibliography** page. See **Tool A5** to learn how to list your sources.

R Check your poster for spelling. Remember it's a tool you will use during the entire theme! Does it represent the theme? At the bottom of the poster, write down three ideas you would like to explore in this theme.

C
Tales Told by Water

C.1
Tell Me of Your Travels, Water!

(SD: Recognize/appreciate individual/group differences in means of expressing ideas. LA: Organize information logically and chronologically in a sequence chart. FA: With predetermined criteria, explore different means of producing sound. Sc: Understand that variations in pitch and intensity are a result of speed and density.)

Brainstorm ideas about where water comes from before it gets to your household tap, and where it travels to after it leaves the sink. Use **Tool A2** to get you started. Once you have your ideas on paper, make a **sequencing chart** (as shown in **Tool A3**) to illustrate the path water follows from its source, through your house, and back to its source. Draw a background for your step-by-step illustration showing the environment around the water (e.g., the plants, your house, different landscapes).

Use a tuning fork to compare sounds made with liquids or solids in the experiment on **STEPSpage 56.**

(LA: Identify/use information collected from appropriate sources to establish relationships. Organize information logically and chronologically in an audio-visual format. FA: Using instruments, identify and produce variations in the parameters of sounds.)

Create a video, filmstrip, or storybook to relate the travels of a drop of water. Before you start your rough copy of the storyline for your audio-visual presentation, decide on which format you will use to present your final version. Use **Tool D1** to plan your final project. **Tool D10** offers ideas on how to make a video and **Tool C7** tells how to make a storybook.

Then look back on the ideas you brainstormed to develop a plan for your story. **Tool A3** has a **sequencing chart** that can help you put your ideas in order. **Tool E3** can help you write a paragraph about each image in your sequence. Use **Tool C8** to review your work.

To create sound effects, use bottles of water filled to different depths as in the experiment on **STEPSpage 57.** Improvise a piece of music using the form A-B-A. This simply means that you start with one type of sound (A) (e.g., a wind instrument), followed by another type of sound (B) (e.g., a percussion instrument), and then finish with the first sound (A). You may wish to experiment with other series or combinations of instruments. See **Tool B3** for ideas on how to evaluate your musical creation.

E.1 (LA: Identify/use information from a text to extrapolate ideas for an imaginary story. Demonstrate an understanding of language conventions.)

Imagine that one day you were having fun blowing soap bubbles. You made this huge bubble. It was even bigger than you. Suddenly, a gust of wind blew the bubble over you, but didn't pop it. You found yourself inside the bubble and blowing in the wind! After blowing over houses and trees, lakes and meadows, you noticed a little boy looking at you. He asked you where you were coming from and where you were heading. Tell him your story and where you would like to go from here with your bubble.

Write your ideas using the sequence chart described in **Tool A3** and then develop each idea into a paragraph using **Tool E3**.

OR

E.2 (FA: Using instruments, identify and produce variations in the intensity and the parameters of sounds. With a group, create an original selection of music.)

Create a musical interpretation of water. See **STEPSpage 58** and **Tool B3**.

R (SD: Recognize and examine differences in communicating ideas and in the ability to take initiatives.)

In your *Thoughtsteps Journal*, write comparisons between water and music. Your answers may not seem scientific at all. Focus on images, feelings, and sensations since it is difficult to find concrete comparisons between music and water. Use **Tools D1** and **A9** to comment on the results.

If you used other **Toolbox** cards, complete the corresponding evaluation forms and include them in your *Thoughtsteps Journal*.

C

Tales Told
by Water

C.1

Tell Me of
Your Travels,
Water!

USE A TUNING FORK TO COMPARE SOUNDS

MADE WITH LIQUIDS OR SOLIDS

(Sc: Understand that variations in pitch and intensity are a result of speed and density. FA: With predetermined criteria, explore different means of producing sound.)

Write the report for this experiment using **Tool C5**.

MATERIALS REQUIRED:
- a bowl of water
- a tuning fork

PROCEDURE:
1. Tap the tines of the tuning fork against a hard surface.
2. Place the ball end of the fork against the surface of a table so that you can listen to, and watch, the vibrations of the tines on the tuning fork. Record your observations.
3. Repeat these last two steps, placing the ball end of the fork on objects that are solid, hollow, etc. (Test the fork against different instruments to change the pitch of the sound produced: guitar, piano, xylophone, drum, etc.) For each trial, record your observations.
4. This time, tap the tuning fork again, but place one of the tines in the bowl of water. Keep the other tine above the water's surface. Record your observations.

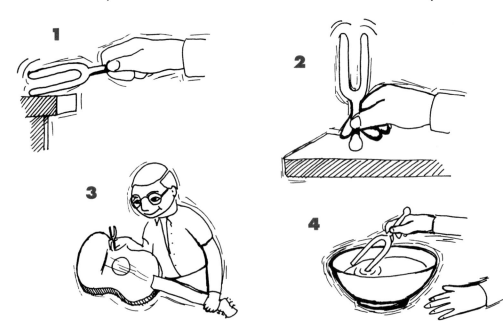

OBSERVATIONS:
What happens to the tuning fork when it is held against different objects? What happens to the fork in water?

CONCLUSION:
Water is a liquid capable of conducting sound. All solid surfaces are able to act as sound conductors. Sound travels in waves that become visible in water. How do different instruments transmit sound? How can you alter the pitch?

CREATE A MELODY USING BOTTLES OF WATER
FILLED TO DIFFERENT DEPTHS
(FA: Using instruments, identify and produce variations in the parameters of sounds.)

Write the report for this experiment using **Tool C5**.

C

Tales Told
by Water

C.1

*Tell Me of
Your Travels,
Water!*

MATERIALS:
- 7 identical bottles with a narrow opening
- water
- a stick

PROCEDURE:
1. Pour water into each of the bottles so that there is more water in the second bottle than in the first, more water in the third than in the second, etc.
2. Blow gently across the top of the bottles by placing your bottom lip on the neck of the bottle. Then try tapping each bottle with a chopstick. Record your observations for both techniques.
3. Now try creating your own melodies.

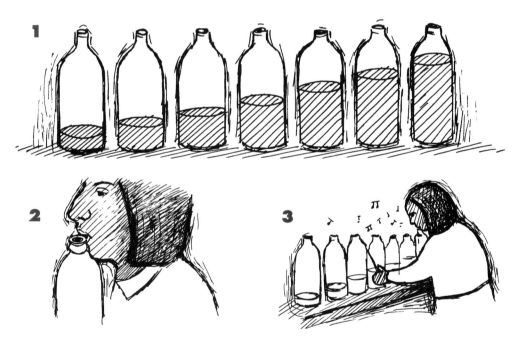

OBSERVATIONS:
How do the sounds differ when you play the bottles like a wind instrument or like a percussion instrument?

CONCLUSION:
How can you explain the different sounds obtained from your bottles? What other variations can you think of for playing the bottles? In addition to the conclusions listed in your preparation experiment, what conclusions can you make about water and sound?

C

Tales Told
by Water

C.1

Tell Me of
Your Travels,
Water!

E.2 CREATE A MUSICAL INTERPRETATION OF WATER

(FA: Using instruments, identify and produce variations in the intensity and the parameters of sounds. With a group, create an original selection of music.)

Use **Tool B3** to prepare and evaluate your musical creations. **Tool E1** will give you the definitions for the musical terms used in this activity.

1. Choose body percussion movements, voice, or instruments to represent the different sounds of water when it's:

   raining gently   pouring rain
   flowing in a small stream   flowing in a river
   rolling in ocean waves   crashing its waves against the rocks
   splashing in a fountain   tumbling over a waterfall

2. Choose a group to do this activity with you. Divide your group into two smaller groups: A and B.

3. Have group A play falling rain: softly at first (dolce), crescendo (growing louder), forte (very loud), decrescendo (growing softer) and ending softly. This is the "A" pattern or the background music for your entire rondo and should make up 16 counts or beats of music.

4. Have group B play the water on the ground: dolce (for the ribbons of water trickling over the ground), mezzo dolce (for the stream), forte (for the rushing creek or the waterfalls) and then dolce again (for the wide, slow river). This is the "B" pattern of your rondo and should also make up 16 counts or beats of music.

5. Now put the two patterns together in an A-B-A form, where group A plays first, then group B and group A finishes the pattern by repeating the same movement played at the start.

6. Have group B add a new movement (the "C" pattern) with a different interpretation of water in motion.

7. This time, when you assemble the music, use a rondo form (A-B-A-C-A) with 16 beats for each section. Group A plays the refrain. Group B plays its first interpretation (B) after group A has played for 16 beats. Group B then stops playing for 16 beats while group A plays the refrain again. Group B then plays its second interpretation (C). Group A completes the rondo by playing a final 16 beats of music. Record your creations.

8. To extend this activity you might like to listen to musical selections that have been written to represent flowing water or that have incorporated natural sounds of water in the music.

Here are a few suggestions:

William Tell Overture - "The Storm" by Rossini (this can be viewed in an animated orchestra with Mickey Mouse in Walt Disney's **Silly Symphonies**)

"Night on Bare Mountain" by Mussorgski (scene from **Fantasia**)

"Cloudy" by Paul Simon

Carnival of the Animals -"Aquarium" by Camille St. Saëns

"River" by Bill Staines

"Rain, Rain, Go Away" by Peter, Paul and Mary (medley of nursery rhymes based on a rainy afternoon).

DISCUSSION QUESTIONS:
How is an orchestra able to create textures in music? Why does a rainstorm have a soft-loud-soft shape to its sound? How is a musical scale like a water cycle? What instruments/vocal sounds/body percussions most effectively create images of water?

C

Tales Told
by Water

C.1

*Tell Me of
Your Travels,
Water!*

C

Tales Told by Water

C.2

Come Swim My Cycle

(SD: Recognize/appreciate individual/group differences in means of expressing ideas. LA: Identify/use information from a text to predict, infer and extrapolate outcomes.)

Use **Tool A1** to explore what you already know about the cycle of water by discussing or reflecting on this idea: Thousands of years ago, a human being drank water from a stream. This morning, could you have been drinking the same water? Could it be that you both drank the same water? How could water consumed many years ago find its way back to the same stream? How could water that was polluted 20 years ago be pure today? Where does water on earth come from? Where does the rain come from?

(LA: Identify/use information from text/images to synthesize ideas in an illustration. Sc: Understand the phases in the water cycle. Study different forms of energy production and uses. Understand that matter can be transformed through physical or chemical reaction.)

Before reading the story "Mousna, Prisoner in a Droplet", on **pages 35** to **44** of *Discovering Wind and Water*, look at the illustrations and the title. Can they help you find some of the answers about the water cycle? After reading the adventure, copy the three illustrations on **STEPSpage 62** into your *Thoughtsteps Journal*. Label each illustration with the different stages in the water cycle that you discovered in the story. To evaluate your reading skills in this activity, see **Tool C1**.

As a second activity, research and draw a poster showing the stages in transforming water into energy through hydro-electricity. See **STEPSpage 63** and **Tool C4** and **D1**. From your poster, create a 3-D model of the stages, using **Tool D1**.

(Sc: Understand that matter can be transformed through physical or chemical reaction. Understand the phases in the water cycle.)

See **Tool C5**, before you do the following experiments. Record the results of your experiments in your *Thoughtsteps Journal*:

E.1 Experiment to learn how water is filtered on **STEPSpage 64**.
Or

E.2 Experiment to learn how water evaporates on **STEPSpage 65**.
Or

E.3 Experiment to learn about liquids and their densities on **STEPSpage 67**.
Or

E.4 Experiment with water pressure on **STEPSpage 68**.
Or

E.5 Experiment to learn how water condenses to form clouds on **STEPSpage 69**.

E.6 (FA: Formulate a dialogue from a given theme. Use appropriate gestures, voice, and special effects. In a positive manner, support the roles played by others.)

Read Mousna's story with a partner or divide the reading among several friends. Then break the story into parts and act it out in front of the class using a narrator, actors, and sound effects. Use **Tools B2** and **B3** to prepare your presentation.

(Sc: Draw conclusions by describing and comparing the data/information collected.)

Once you have completed the story of Mousna and your experiment(s) with water, take a few minutes to write in your *Thoughtsteps Journal* what you learned about water and its cycle. See **Tools C4, C5,** and **D1**.

If you used other **Toolbox** cards, complete the corresponding evaluation forms and include them in your *Thoughtsteps Journal*.

ILLUSTRATE THE WATER CYCLE

(LA: Identify/use information from text/images to synthesize ideas in an illustration. Sc: Understand the phases in the water cycle. Study different forms of energy production and uses. Understand that matter can be transformed through physical or chemical reaction.)

Copy these three illustrations into your *Thoughtsteps Journal*. Label each illustration with a different stage of the water cycle, based on the information in the story "Mousna, Prisoner in a Droplet", on **pages 35** to **44** of *Discovering Wind and Water*.

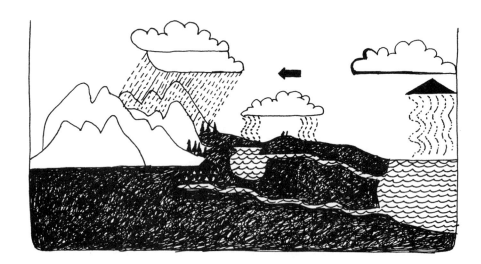

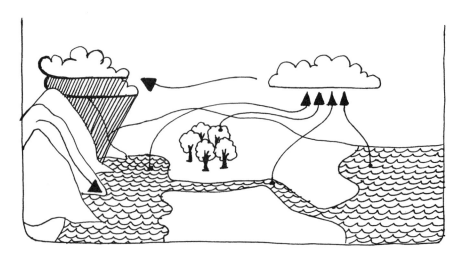

(LA: Identify/use information from text/images to synthesize ideas in an illustration. Sc: Understand the phases in the water cycle. Study different forms of energy production and uses. Understand that matter can be transformed through physical or chemical reaction.)

As a second activity, research and draw a poster and then design a model to show the stages in transforming water into energy through hydro-electricity.

Using **Tool A1**, think about what would have to happen to change a quantity of water into electricity for a lightbulb. Use the sequencing chart below to illustrate your ideas. Start the sequence with a drawing of water and end with a drawing of a lit lightbulb. Write a brief explanation under each illustrated step. Then check your theories by researching information about hydro-electric power plants and dams. See **Tool C4**.

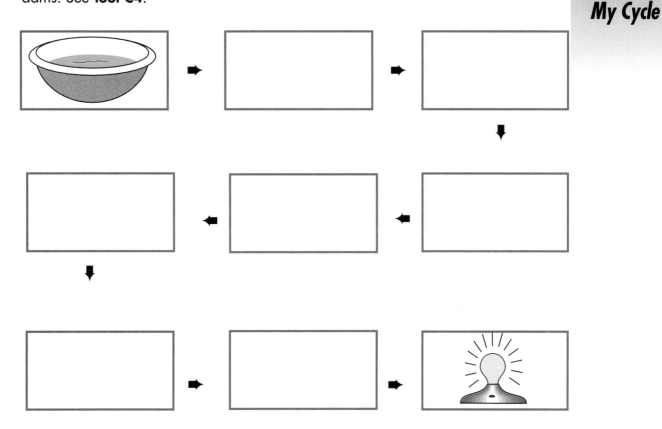

Using the information from your research, you can also prepare a 3-D model of a hydro-electric plant or other method to generate electricity with water. Include written texts to explain the different stages. **Tool D1** can help you prepare your model and **Tool C8** will help you edit your texts before writing your final copy.

E.1 EXPERIMENT TO LEARN HOW WATER IS FILTERED

(Sc: Understand that matter can be transformed through physical or chemical reaction. Understand the phases in the water cycle.)

If you pour water on the ground, it will disappear from the surface and into the ground through a process called infiltration. Does this help to clean the water? Write down your hypothesis before continuing with this experiment.

Use the format in **Tool C5** to complete this experiment.

MATERIALS REQUIRED:

• a pail of muddy water	• some sand
• a paper coffee filter	• some gravel
• a transparent plastic bottle (2l pop bottle)	• some crushed charcoal

PROCEDURE:

1. Ask an adult to help you cut off the top of the bottle. BE CAREFUL HERE!
2. Invert the top of the bottle and place the neck inside the bottle.
3. Place the coffee filter inside the bottle neck and fill it with, first, a layer of gravel, followed by a layer of charcoal, and a layer of sand.
4. Slowly pour the muddy water into the filter.

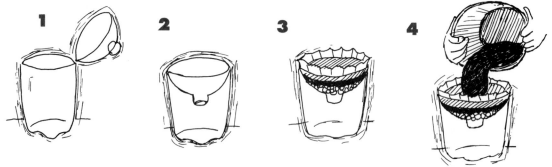

OBSERVATIONS:

How is the water in the bottle different from the water in the pail?

CONCLUSION:

When water filters into the ground, it passes through layers of dirt, sand, gravel, etc. before returning to the stream. How does this experiment compare with what happens in nature? Were the results what you expected in your hypothesis?

Here are a few other questions you might like to explore:
- If you changed the order of the layers, would the water be cleaner?
- Could the colour of the sand change the results of your filtration process?
- What is the role of each layer in the filter? Try them separately to find out.
- How is the water in your community, town, or city purified so that you can drink it?

E.2 EXPERIMENT TO LEARN HOW WATER EVAPORATES

(Sc: Understand that matter can be transformed through physical or chemical reaction. Understand the phases in the water cycle.)

You have surely noticed that the water level in lakes goes down in the summer. What happens to the water? Write down your hypothesis before continuing with this experiment.
Use the format in **Tool C5** to complete this experiment. **Tool E6** has suggestions for checking your measurements.

MATERIALS REQUIRED:
- 5 rectangular containers of the same size   • water
- 5 thermometers

PROCEDURE:
1. Measure the width (w), and length (l) of your containers in centimetres. Calculate their surface areas by multiplying (w)x(l). Record the areas (in cm^2) in your observations.
2. Fill each container with the same amount of water. Measure the height (or depth) of the water in centimetres (cm). In your observations, record the volume of water in each container. To calculate the volume (cm^3) of water, multiply the surface area of the container by the height of the water.
3. Place a thermometer in each container and record the temperatures after 5 minutes.
4. Place each container in a different area for at least 24 hours or for up to 3 days (72 hours) (e.g., in the refrigerator, near a heat source, in the sun).
5. Record the temperatures again at the end of your experiment. Then measure the water left in each container. Calculate the volume of water left in each container.

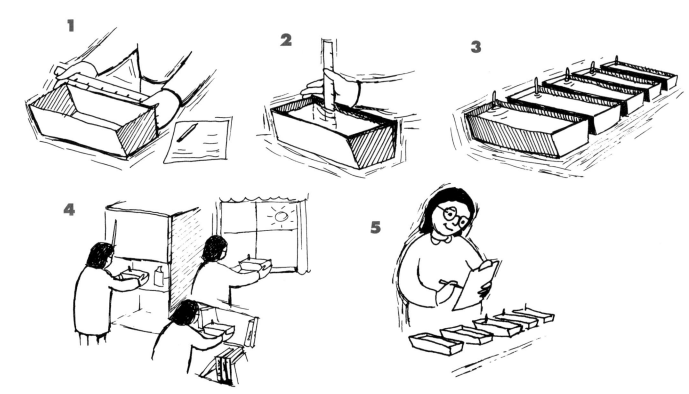

Tales Told by Water

C.2

Come Swim My Cycle

OBSERVATIONS:
Complete this chart as you do your experiment:

Container and location	Area (in cm²)	Depth (in cm)	Volume (in cm³)	Temperature (in °C)	Depth (in cm)	Volume (in cm³)	Temperature (in °C)
			AT THE START:			**AT THE END:**	
1-							
2-							
3-							
4-							
5-							

CONCLUSION:
What differences did you notice in the amount of water in each container at the start and at the end of the experiment? How do the differences compare with the temperature of the room or space? Are there other factors to think about in your results?

Here are a few other ideas to explore:
- How could you prevent water from evaporating?
- How could you recover (get back) water that evaporates?
- Could your method of recovery be used for other purposes?
- Would the results have been different if the surface areas of each container were different?
- Can you think of another way to calculate the amount of water in each container?

E.3 EXPERIMENT TO LEARN ABOUT LIQUIDS AND THEIR DENSITIES

(Sc: Understand that matter can be transformed through physical or chemical reaction. Understand the phases in the water cycle.)

Do you think that water has weight? How much do you think a litre of water would weigh? Would it weigh the same amount as a litre of vegetable oil or milk or other liquid? Write down your hypothesis before continuing with this experiment.
Use the format in **Tool C5** to complete this experiment. **Tool E6** has suggestions for checking your measurements.

MATERIALS REQUIRED:

- a scale
- 3 identical containers (at least 1 litre capacity)
- 1 litre of water, milk, vegetable oil or other liquid

PROCEDURE:

1. Weigh each container on the scale and record its weight. Be sure to note any differences.
2. Fill each container with exactly one litre of milk, water, or oil. Record the weights. Remember to subtract the weight of the container.

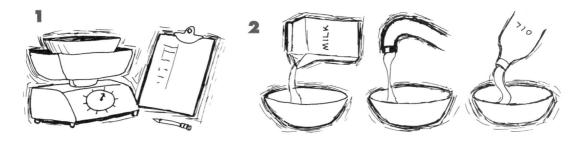

OBSERVATIONS:

Complete the following chart:

CONTAINER OF	WEIGHT FULL	WEIGHT EMPTY	WEIGHT OF LIQUID
1- water			
2- milk			
3- vegetable oil			
4-			
5-			

CONCLUSION:

How do the weights of the liquids compare? How do your results compare with your hypothesis?

Here are a few ideas to explore further:
How much does a litre of fresh water weigh? Does a litre of salt water weigh the same as a litre of fresh water? Why is there a difference in weight when all of the substances are liquids?

E.4 EXPERIMENT WITH WATER PRESSURE

(Sc: Understand that matter can be transformed through physical or chemical reaction. Understand the phases in the water cycle.)

Why is it that water moves from place to place? Why does it move more quickly in some rivers than in others? Why are the currents different? Write down your hypothesis before continuing with this experiment.

Use the format in **Tool C5** to complete this experiment.

MATERIALS REQUIRED:
- 2 tin cans
- a nail
- a hammer
- water
- 2 flat bottomed basins or containers (at least 60 cm x 60 cm)
- a waterproof marker or pencil

PROCEDURE:
1. Using the hammer and nail, pierce four holes horizontally at the same height around one of the cans, 1/3 of the way from the bottom. With the other can, pierce the four holes vertically (one above the other).
2. Place one of the cans in the centre of each basin.
3. Fill the first can to the brim with water. On the side of the basin, mark with your pencil or marker where the water leaving the can hits the basin.
4. Do the same with the second can.

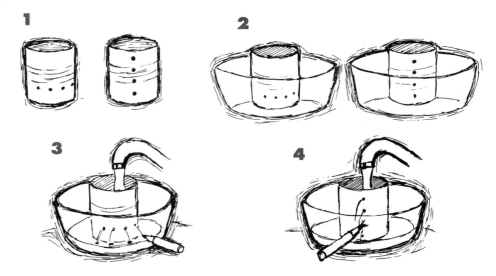

OBSERVATIONS:
Illustrate what you observed.

CONCLUSION:
Can you explain why water moves from one place to another at different speeds? Can you explain in your own words what water pressure is? Do you know of any machines or instruments that operate on water pressure? Explain how they work.

.5 EXPERIMENT TO LEARN HOW WATER CONDENSES TO FORM CLOUDS

(Sc: Understand that matter can be transformed through physical or chemical reaction. Understand the phases in the water cycle.)

C

Tales Told
by Water

C.2

Come Swim
My Cycle

The water that evaporates from lakes and rivers falls back to earth in the form of rain. Can you explain this process? Write down your hypothesis before continuing with this experiment.

Use the format in **Tool C5** to complete this experiment.

MATERIALS REQUIRED:
• a kettle
• water
• a container filled with ice cubes

PROCEDURE:
1. Fill the kettle and bring the water to a boil. Turn off the element.
2. Put on mitts or gloves. Hold the container of ice cubes over the steam coming from the kettle. Be careful not to burn yourself.

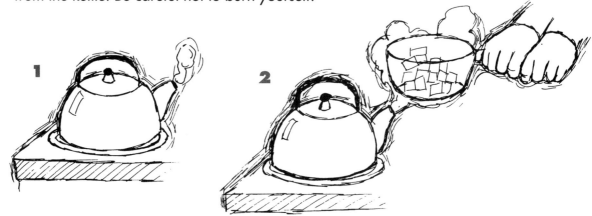

OBSERVATIONS:
Illustrate what you observed. Remember to label your illustrations and explain them.

CONCLUSION:
Where did the water under the container come from? How was it formed? Why does water vapour (steam) change into drops of water? If the container was filled with cold water, would you obtain the same results? Do your results agree with your hypothesis? How does this experiment relate to the water cycle in nature?

C
Tales Told by Water

C.3

Hello Raindrop! Where Have You Been?

(SD: Recognize/appreciate individual/group differences in means of expressing ideas. LA: Identify/use information from ideas/text to select characteristics, evaluate relationships, and summarize ideas in a poster. FA: Design a poster to represent certain facets of the environment.)

Using the problem-solving approach from **Tool A1**, explore what you already know about water by discussing these questions with a partner or with a group of friends:
- When is water a liquid/a solid/a gas?
- What role does water play in our bodies?
- Is ocean water like lake or river water?

Choose one of the questions and design a poster to show what you know about the question, using **Tools D1** and **D9**. Create a display area in your class for your posters. You could call this corner: **Discovering Water from All Angles** or **Water under the Looking Glass** or ...?

(LA: Identify/use information from ideas/text to select characteristics, evaluate relationships, and summarize ideas in a poster. Sc: Identify and compare the physical properties of matter. Understand that matter can be transformed through physical or chemical reaction. FA: Design or modify a poster to represent certain facets of the environment.)

Read the story "Hello, Raindrop! Where Have You Been?", **pages 44** to **48** in *Discovering Wind and Water* to gather more information about water, its properties and functions. Once you have read the story, re-examine your poster to see if there is new information that you could add to it, or if there is another poster that you could design. See **Tools D1** and **D9**. If you decide to make a new poster, you might wish to wait until after you have completed some of the extension activities.

E.1 (Sc: Understand the body's need for water.)
Research the role of water in the human body on **STEPSpage 72.**
Or

E.2 (Sc: Understand the relationships between organisms and their environment.)
Research an aquatic animal on **STEPSpage 72.**
Or

E.3-5 (Sc: Identify and compare the physical properties of matter.)

E.3 Construct a simple densimeter on **STEPSpage 73.**
Or

E.4 Experiment with the densities of liquids on **STEPSpage 75.**
Or

E.5 Experiment with fresh and salt water densities on **STEPSpage 76.**
Or

E.6-7 (Sc: Understand that matter can be transformed through physical or chemical reaction.)

E.6 Experiment with how water can change from a liquid to a solid on **STEPSpage 77**.

Or

E.7 Experiment with methods for purifying water on **STEPS page 78**.

Or

E.8 (FA: Formulate a dialogue from a given theme. Use appropriate gestures, voice, and special effects. In a positive manner, support the roles played by others.)

Using **Tools B2** and **B3**, present a part of the story, **Hello, Raindrop! Where Have You Been?** as a play with a narrator and actors.

(Sc: Identify and compare the physical properties of matter. Understand that matter can be transformed through chemical or physical reaction. LA: Identify/use information from text/images to evaluate relationships and question the premises for them. SD: Identify and develop means of improving effective communication.)

Are you ready to check your knowledge on the properties and functions of water? If so, use your *Thoughtsteps Journal* to record your answers to the questions on **STEPSpage 79**. If you're not sure, review the posters and the story in this activity.

If you used the **Toolbox** cards, complete the corresponding evaluation forms and include them in your *Thoughtsteps Journal*.

C

Tales Told
by Water

C.3

*Hello
Raindrop!
Where Have
You Been?*

𝓔.1 RESEARCH THE ROLE OF WATER IN THE HUMAN BODY

(Sc: Understand the body's need for water.)

Use **Tool C4** to prepare your research projects. Use **Tool C8** to edit your work.

Humans need water to survive. Every human being needs to consume at least 2.5 litres of water every day. This water replaces the water lost through perspiration, respiration (breathing), and elimination. As you can see, water is very important for our bodies. Research the answers to the following questions:
- How is it that we consume 2 or more litres of water daily without drinking 2 litres of water per day? Where does all the water come from?
- What is the percentage of water in our bodies?
- What role does water play in making our bodies function?

𝓔.2 RESEARCH INFORMATION ABOUT AN AQUATIC ANIMAL

(Sc: Understand the relationships between organisms and their environment.)

Use **Tool C4** to prepare your research project. Use **Tool C8** to edit your work.

Is it possible to find the same kinds of fish in the oceans/the rivers/the lakes? Complete the chart below listing the fish that live in fresh water and in salt water.

FRESH WATER FISH	SALT WATER FISH

Choose one fresh water fish and one salt water fish. Study the similarities and differences between them. Examine their appearance, external and internal parts, their method of reproduction, their natural habitats, their food sources, etc.

Use the information you gathered and **Tool D1** to prepare a 3-D display on both fish. A shoe box or other box turned on its side could hold all of your information (a suspended model of the fish and its food sources, background pictures of their natural habitats, and written texts and titles).

E.3 CONSTRUCT A SIMPLE DENSIMETER

(Sc: Identify and compare the physical properties of matter.)

C

Tales Told
by Water

C.3

Hello
Raindrop!
Where Have
You Been?

An instrument that measures the density of a liquid is called a densimeter.
Here's how you can build a simple one.

Use the format in **Tool C5** to complete this experiment. **Tool E6** has suggestions
for checking your measurements.

MATERIALS REQUIRED:

- a test tube
- adhesive tape
- different liquids: salt water, milk, juice, vinegar, oil, syrup, etc.
- coins or sand or lead weights
- a large container of water
- a ruler and a waterproof pen

PROCEDURE:

1. Tape a strip of adhesive tape, along the side of the test tube.
2. Place a few coins or weights or sand in the bottom of the test tube.
3. Balance the test tube in the container of water.
4. Add weights if necessary to make the densimeter float upright in the water.
5. With your waterproof pen, mark the level of water on the densimeter.
6. Remove the test-tube and wipe it dry. Write the number 10 next to the mark you made on the test tube.
7. With your ruler and pen, mark new lines at one centimetre intervals above and below the number 10 mark. Write the numbers 11, 12, 13, etc. above the 10 and 9, 8, 7, etc. below.
8. Try placing your densimeter in different liquids. Don't put your densimeter in a liquid you want to drink afterwards.

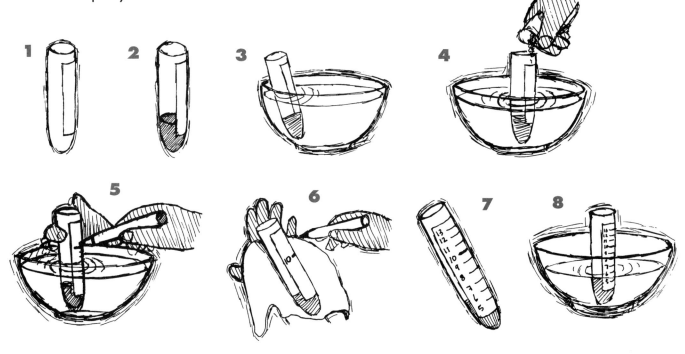

C
Tales Told by Water

C.3
Hello Raindrop! Where Have You Been?

OBSERVATIONS:

Record the densities of the liquids you test with your densimeter.

LIQUID	DENSITY	COMPARISON TO WATER
- Water	10	0
-		
-		
-		

CONCLUSION:

What have you learned about the densities of different liquids? Does a liquid's density relate to its weight? How could you test this question?

E.4 EXPERIMENT WITH THE DENSITIES OF LIQUIDS

(Sc: Identify and compare the physical properties of matter.)

C

Tales Told
by Water

C.3

*Hello
Raindrop!
Where Have
You Been?*

Here is another experiment to demonstrate how water differs in density compared to other liquids. It is difficult to show this to a large group. You might consider performing your experiment on video so that you can show it to others more easily.

Use the format in **Tool C5** to complete this experiment.

MATERIALS REQUIRED:
• a jar with a wide-mouthed opening
• corn syrup, water, vegetable oil, rubbing alcohol
• food colouring
• a funnel (you can make one with a piece of Bristol board or manila tag)
• small, light-weight objects (a piece of candle, a piece of wood, a mothball, etc.)

PROCEDURE:
1. Pour 5 cm of corn syrup into the jar without touching the sides.
2. Add a few drops of food colouring to some water.
3. Place your funnel in the jar so that it is touching the side of the jar just above the surface of the syrup. Slowly and carefully pour the water into the funnel.
4. Repeat step 3 with the vegetable oil and the alcohol.
5. Carefully introduce your small objects, one at a time, into the jar to see where they will float.

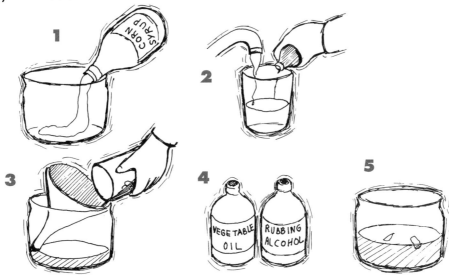

OBSERVATIONS:
Illustrate the liquids as you see them in the jar. Illustrate also where the objects are floating in suspension in the liquids. Remember to label your illustrations.

CONCLUSION:
What have you learned about liquids and their densities? How does the density of a liquid affect an object's ability to float in this liquid? Can you think of another experiment to show different densities?

E.5 EXPERIMENT WITH FRESH AND SALT WATER DENSITIES

(Sc: Identify and compare the physical properties of matter.)

Salt water and fresh water do not have the same density. Have you ever tried floating in salt water? It's easier to float in salt water than in fresh water. Here is an experiment to demonstrate how density affects buoyancy. It is difficult to show this to a large group. You might consider performing your experiment on video so that you can show it to others more easily.

Use the format in **Tool C5** to complete this experiment.

MATERIALS REQUIRED:

• an egg	• salt
• a large wide-mouthed jar	• a spoon
• water	• a glass

PROCEDURE:

1. Fill the jar half full with tap water.
2. Place the egg on the spoon and lower it carefully into the water.
3. Fill the glass 3/4 full of water. Add salt, stirring after each addition. Keep adding salt until the water is saturated (when the salt no longer dissolves in the water).
4. Carefully pour salt water, a small amount at a time, into the jar. Watch what happens to the egg after each addition of salt water.
5. Try adding a little more fresh water. Record what happens to the egg. Alternate salt water and fresh water or add the rest of your salt water.

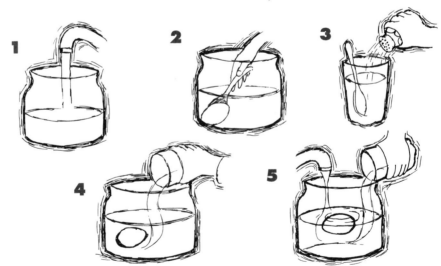

OBSERVATIONS:

Illustrate your observations. Remember to label the illustrations according to whether you added salt water or fresh water.

CONCLUSION:

Can you explain why it is easier to float in salt water? How does the egg resemble an iceberg floating in salt water? Can you think of other objects or living things that might be affected by this principle?

C

Tales Told
by Water

C.3

Hello
Raindrop!
Where Have
You Been?

E.6 EXPERIMENT WITH HOW WATER CAN CHANGE FROM A LIQUID TO A SOLID

(Sc: Understand that matter can be transformed through physical or chemical reaction.)

This experiment is one you can eat! Making popsicles is not only a lot of fun, but can also teach an important physical property of water.

Use the format in **Tool C5** to complete this experiment.

MATERIALS REQUIRED:

- a paper cup
- frozen fruit juice or fruit juice concentrate
- a popsicle stick
- a thin piece of cardboard slightly larger than the cup's opening
- water
- a pair of scissors

PROCEDURE:

1. Fill the cup half full with fruit juice concentrate.
2. Add water to within 1 centimetre of the top of the cup. Mark the outside of the cup to show where the surface of the liquid is.
3. Mix the water and the juice concentrate with your popsicle stick.
4. Cut a slit into the centre of your cardboard. Place it over the cup and slide the popsicle stick through the slit.
5. Trim the edges of the cardboard.
6. Place your cup in the freezer for at least 6 hours.
7. When you remove the cardboard, be sure to look at the space between the popsicle and the top of the cup BEFORE you remove the popsicle. Now you can eat the popsicle!

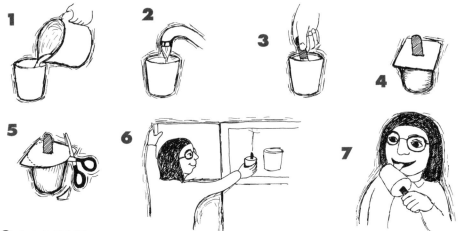

OBSERVATIONS:

Draw the steps in your experiment, being sure to mark the air space before and after you froze your popsicle.

CONCLUSION:

What did you learn about water in this experiment? Did you know that water is the only substance that expands when it freezes? All other liquids contract when they change to a solid state. How is this principle important in everyday life in the kitchen?

C

Tales Told
by Water

C.3

*Hello
Raindrop!
Where Have
You Been?*

$E_{.7}$ EXPERIMENT WITH METHODS FOR PURIFYING WATER

(Sc: Understand that matter can be transformed through physical or chemical reaction.)

How can salt water become pure water? Here is just one way to do it.

Use the format in **Tool C5** to complete this experiment.

MATERIALS REQUIRED:

• a large bowl	• salt
• a small bowl or cup	• water
• plastic stretch wrap	• a spoon

PROCEDURE:

1. Mix the water and salt in the large bowl.
2. Place the small bowl or cup in the middle of the bowl. If it can't sit on the bottom without floating, you will need to pour out some of your salt water.
3. Cover the large bowl with plastic stretch wrap.
4. Place the spoon (or another small weighted object) in the centre of the wrap, so that the wrap slopes toward the cup in the centre.
5. Set the bowl in a warm place for two or three days. Watch what happens to the plastic wrap and the cup.
6. At the end of the experiment, remove the plastic wrap and taste the water in the cup.

OBSERVATIONS:

Illustrate what you see. Remember to label your illustrations and describe what you observe.

CONCLUSION:

What is different about the water in the cup at the end of the experiment? Can you think of another way of purifying water?

(Sc: Identify and compare the physical properties of matter. Understand that matter can be transformed through chemical or physical reaction. LA: Identify/use information from text/images to evaluate relationships and question the premises for them. SD: Identify and develop means of improving effective communication.)

Are you ready to check your knowledge on the properties and functions of water? If so, use your *Thoughtsteps Journal* to record the answers to the following questions. If you're not sure, review the posters and the story in this activity as you answer the questions. Use complete sentences when answering the questions.

1. Why does only fresh water evaporate out of the ocean?

2. What would happen if rain contained salt water? Give at least one example.

3. Would drinking salt water cause human tissues to swell or shrink? Explain your answer.

4. The process described in question 3 is called osmosis. Look up the definition for osmosis in your dictionary and write it down.

5. What is condensation? Give an example to explain your answer.

6. What happens to water when it is heated? What is this process called?

7. What is filtration? Give an example of filtration.

8. How does the density of salt water compare with the density of fresh water? Give an example to describe how the two compare.

9. Name three properties that describe the differences between fresh water and salt water. (Note that a property of water is a scientist's way of describing or identifying what water is.) Give an example for each property.

10. Describe one experiment that you tried. Tell what you did, what you observed, and what you learned from the experiment.

Do you have other questions, answers, or comments that you would like to add?

As an optional exercise to examine your writing skills, use **Tool E2** to help you identify the noun(s) and verb(s) in each answer. If you're missing one or the other, then there's a chance that the answer is not a complete sentence.

C

Tales Told by Water

C.4

All That Water Just for Me?

(Sc: Use the scientific process to make observations by collecting data. Ma: Use metric units/instruments to measure volume and capacity.)

Measure the amount of water you consume in a day. See **STEPSpage 82** for a description of this experiment. If you are unfamiliar with how to measure volume and capacity, it would be wise to review these concepts in your math textbook or by using **Tool E6**.

(LA: Identify/use information from a text to establish cause/effect relationships. Ma: Use problem-solving strategies to collect data. Construct and interpret graphs to represent data collected. SD: Understand the importance of change as a process for improving the environment.)

Read the statistics (numbers) about how water is used on **page 48** of *Discovering Wind and Water*. On **STEPSpage 83**, there is an example of a graph so that you can see how the water is used. Design a second graph to show the results of your consumption (use of water) in one day (from the preparation activity). Use the information from **page 48** and from both graphs to identify areas where you could reduce the amount of water you use or to note where you are already using less water than the average person. See **Tool D1**. **Tool D5** has suggestions to help you with your graphs.

In your *Thoughtsteps Journal*, identify three ways you could reduce your water consumption. Use **Tool A1** to help you identify how to reach your goals. Then record how well you succeeded for a period of at least five days.

GOAL	PROCESS	OBSERVATION	COMMENT
1.			
2.			
3.			

At the end of your trial period, comment on how well you did. (Don't be afraid to admit it if in some areas you didn't reach your goal. It is hard to change your lifestyle. It can take much time and effort.)

E.1 (Ma: Use problem-solving strategies to demonstrate the process for completing calculations of volume and capacity.)

Use your math textbook to review exercises where you are asked to calculate sums or averages or where you solve problems about capacity (litres). Or, using **Tool A1**, make up problems and share them with a friend!

Or

E.2 (Sc: Use the scientific process to make observations by organizing/illustrating events. Recognize that humans can have the power to make choices to conserve and protect the environment. LA: Organize selected images and text logically and chronologically.)

Design a chart or model to demonstrate the stages in purifying drinking water. See **Tool D1**. Do you know how the water in your area is filtered before you drink it? Do you know how it is cleaned or purified before going back to its source (river, lake, ocean)? Contact the municipal department responsible for public works to find out. See **Tool A4.**

Or

E.3 (LA: Use context clues to determine the meanings of words: prefixes.)
Can you find the meanings of these "watery" words: *aquamarine, aquanaut, aquaplane, aquarelle, aquarium, aqueduct, aqueous, aquatic, aquiculture, hydraulics, hydroelectric, hydrofoil, hydrography, hydrometer, hydrophobia, hydrothermal, hydroscope*? Find other words in the dictionary containing the root words *aqua* or *hydro* (*hydra*).

(SD: Understand the importance of change as a process for improving the environment.)
In your *Thoughtsteps Journal*, make a closing comment about how this activity has affected your ideas and habits about water consumption. Consult your evaluations from **Tools D5** and **A1**.

C
Tales Told
by Water

C.4
*All
That Water
Just
for Me?*

C

Tales Told
by Water

C.4

*All
That Water
Just
for Me?*

MEASURE THE AMOUNT OF WATER YOU USE IN A DAY

(Sc: Use the scientific process to make observations by collecting data. Ma: Use metric units/instruments to measure volume and capacity.)

Record your water consumption (how much water you use) in a chart similar to the one below. Prepare your report for this experiment using **Tool C5**.

| Estimation of how much water you consume in one day: ▬▬▬▬▬ litres. |
| Test time: (see explanation below on measuring running water) ▬▬▬ sec/1 l. |

ACTIVITIES USING WATER	NO. OF LITRES CONSUMED	NO. OF TIMES/DAY ACTIVITY REPEATED	TOTAL LITRES CONSUMED
drinking water			
washing hands			
flushing the toilet			
washing dishes			
brushing teeth			
bathing/showering			
other:			
Total water consumed in a day: ▬▬▬▬ litres			

MEASURING RUNNING WATER:

Use a 1-litre container to record your water consumption. Record the time it takes to fill your container with one litre of water. Then, each time you use water during the school day, record the time the water is running. Divide this time by the time you recorded to find out how many litres of water were used. E.g., if your container fills in 7 seconds and you wash your hands under running water for 21 seconds, 21 divided by 7 equals 3, so you have consumed or used about 3 litres of water.

MEASURING WATER IN A CONTAINER:

Another way to measure water that sits in a container (like your bathtub, the tank behind your toilet, or the kitchen sink) is to measure the **width** and **length** of the container, as well as the **height** of the water in the container in **decimeters** (1/10 of a meter) and multiply these three numbers to obtain the number of litres in the container. E.g., the tank for the toilet measures 1.5 x 4.5 dm and holds 1.5 dm of water for a total of 10.125 dm or 10 1/4 litres. Each time you flush the toilet, you use about 10 litres of water.

READ FACTS ABOUT WATER CONSUMPTION

(LA: Identify/use information from a text to establish cause/effect relationships. Ma: Use problem-solving strategies to collect data. Construct and interpret graphs to represent data collected. SD: Understand the importance of change as a process for improving the environment.)

Use the information in the facts on **page 48** of *Discovering Wind and Water* to identify areas where you could reduce the amount of water you use. Here is an example of how you could graph the information in the text so that you can clearly see where the most water is used. For other graphics ideas, see **Tool D5**.

C

Tales Told
by Water

C.4

*All
That Water
Just
for Me?*

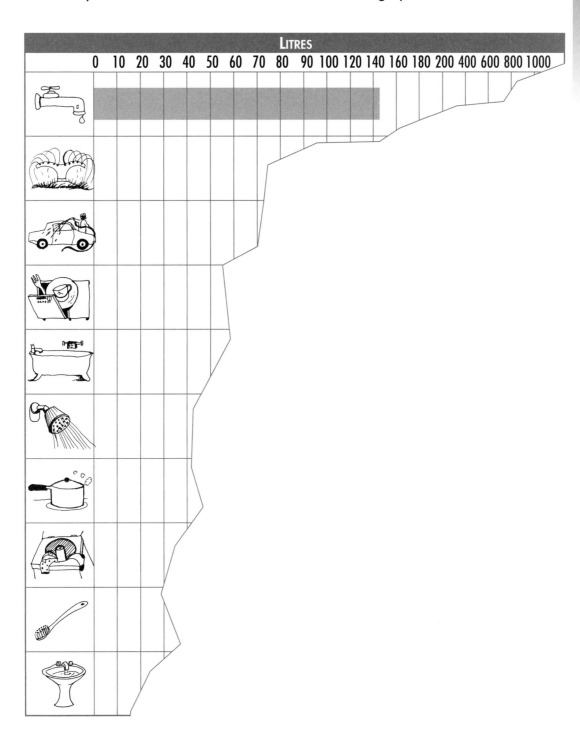

C
Tales Told by Water

C.5
Making Careers Out of Water

(SD: Recognize/appreciate individual/group differences in means of expressing ideas. LA: Identify/use information from text/notes to classify ideas, and establish relationships.)

Brainstorm a list of careers and professions related to water. Using **Tools A2** and **A3**, make a chart listing as many careers and professions as you can. Group them into the following categories:
- jobs involving water as a natural resource;
- jobs involving water as a source of energy;
- jobs involving water conservation;
- jobs involving water as a means of transportation.

If you are working with several people, divide into teams and have each team research one of the categories and then present its ideas to the others. See **Tool C4**.

(LA: Identify/use information from appropriate sources to synthesize in a simple research report. Organize information logically and chronologically. Demonstrate an understanding of language conventions and mechanics. Sc: Develop positive attitudes and skills by examining careers in various fields of science.)

Using **Tool C4**, research a trade or profession related to water and present your information in a career fair. In your presentation, be sure to include the following:
- a description of the job;
- a description of the qualifications needed to do the job;
- an explanation of why you chose to talk about this particular job.

Consult **Tool D1** to evaluate your visual materials. When you are ready to put your career fair together, review **Tool A6** to plan your displays and the space arrangement in your class or wherever you are hosting the career fair.

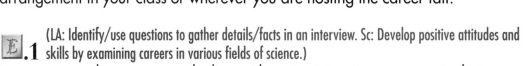
.1 (LA: Identify/use questions to gather details/facts in an interview. Sc: Develop positive attitudes and skills by examining careers in various fields of science.)

In your research on a career dealing with water, interview someone in that career or invite that person to come and talk to your class about his/her job. Use **Tools A4** and **B4** to prepare interview questions before you contact this person.

Or

.2 (LA: Identify/use information from a text to predict or infer meanings and to gather definitions.)

Using the list from your preparation activity, underline the careers that have a clue in their name that they are related to water, e.g., hydroelectric engineer, aquasizes instructor. Then find out what these terms mean. Can you find other careers related to water in the dictionary, the phone book, or at your career fair?

(SD: Identify and develop means of improving process skills: goal setting, planning, achieving, and evaluating.)

Use **Tool A9** to comment on the success of your career fair and what you learned by participating in the activity.

If you used other **Toolbox** cards, complete the corresponding evaluation forms and include them in your *Thoughtsteps Journal*.

Important note: The festival you are about to organize is a culminating activity intended to show others what you learned while working with this centre. **It is important that you complete the preparation stage at the start of your work with this centre.** The number of activities you choose to include in the festival will depend on your time, enthusiasm, numbers (as organizers), and available space. This project is a cooperative one, implying that you will be working in teams on different elements, or tasks. Each team's contributions are essential to the success of the project. Team members are expected to work to the best of their abilities. Good luck! If you would like to share your successes with the authors of this series, please send a description of your project, along with copies of pictures, evaluations, etc. to: **Art Image Publications**. We'll pass your successes along to others at workshops, conferences, and through computer E-mail.

The objectives outlined below apply to all stages of this project. As this is both an opening and a culminating activity encompassing other activities within the centre, the objectives of these other activities have not been repeated.

(SD: Identify, develop, sustain means of improving individual/group:
- acceptance of others' ideas; interaction with others and with the environment;
- organization and use of time; roles, rights, responsibilities within a group;
- problem-solving and decision-making skills; ability to question/evaluate actions;
- risk-taking, motivation, autonomy, confidence; perseverance in spite of obstacles;
- esteem, feelings of belonging and of value; attributes (actual, potential, or desired);
- process skills: goal setting, planning, achieving, and evaluating.

Have you ever been to a festival? If so, describe what you found most interesting, least interesting, or what you would have liked to see included in the festival. Use a PMI chart like the one described in **Tool A3** to help you list your ideas.
- How did you learn about the festival? What publicity was used to announce this event?
- What displays, activities, presentations, exhibits were included in the festival?
- Where was the festival held (inside, outside, in several areas)?
- How was the area for the festival organized? How were the displays/activities divided?
- How was information passed on during the festival (announcements, pamphlets, etc.)?

Once you have completed your PMI chart, examine the *Thoughtsteps Map* to create a list of ideas that could be included in a festival of your own. Compare your ideas with those shown on **STEPSpages 87** and **88**, and divide your ideas into categories. As you complete the activities for this centre, remember that when you prepare your festival, you will need to use the materials and ideas from your activities. **STEPSpages 94** and **95** offer a starter list of other resources you may wish to consult.

Cooperative Project

Organizing and Hosting a Festival

Read the text **Let's Organize a Festival!** on **page 14** of *Discovering Wind and Water*. Use **Tool A6** and the list of ideas generated from the preparation stage to begin plans for your festival. See **STEPSpages 89** and **90** to explore division of teams and roles. See **STEPSpages 91** and **92** to learn how to organize the various layouts for your festival.

E.1 Examine advertising techniques and learn to create display banners. See **STEPSpage 93**.

OR

E.2 Compose a musical selection or a festival theme song to use as part of your publicity campaign. See **Tool B3**.

OR

E.3 Conduct a survey of the people who attend your festival to learn their opinions about the festival. To prepare the questions for your survey, see **Tool A4,** and to compile and examine your results, see **Tools D5** and **D6**.

When the festival is over, take time as a group to evaluate your event.
- Was the organization of the festival effective? Did your advertising campaign work?
- Did each team or individual contribute to the best of his/her/their ability?
- Were your visitors attracted to the areas that you wanted them to see?
- What problems/successes did you encounter along the way? What could you change?
- How could you make use of what you learned in another situation?

Use your **Tool A9** to help you record your thoughts in your *Thoughtsteps Journal.*

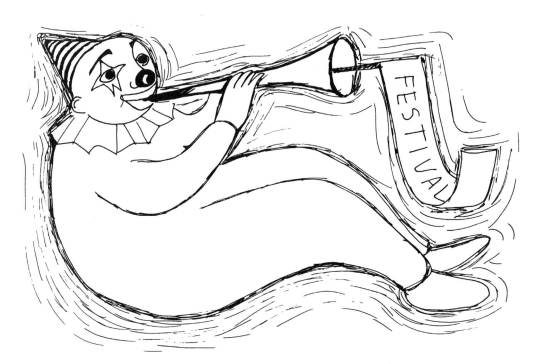

SELECT AND CATEGORIZE THE LEARNING ACTIVITIES IN THIS CENTRE

Using headlines similar to those in the chart below, categorize the options from each of the learning activity paths on the *Thoughtsteps Map*.

DISPLAYS	HANDS-ON ACTIVITIES	DEMONSTRATIONS	AUDIENCE FEED-BACK/SURVEYS

POSSIBLE PRODUCTS FROM THE LEARNING ACTIVITY PATHS IN THE
Discovering Wind and Water **CENTRE**

For a better description of each option, see the Thoughtsteps Map and the explanations in **Steps to** *Discovering Wind and Water*.

A.1   Model hot air balloons; bird's-eye view illustrations; written or taped dialogues about flying in a balloon (these could be performed as skits or dramatic visualizations); collage of flying objects.

A.2   Reports, demonstrations, and hands-on experiments with air and water.

A.3   Research reports about lighter-than-air craft and other topics in aeronautics with jigsaw puzzles about the research; timelines about the evolution of aeronautics.

A.4   Simulations of interviews with pioneers of flight; real interviews with other pioneers in your community.

B.1   Surveys from a Rainy Day Games Event; graphs of survey results; simulation of a rainstorm using musical notes; the best games to present during your festival.

B.2   Research of different inventions for adapting to weather; Inuit sunglasses; designs of clothing for the climate; illustrations and stories about people not prepared for the climate; experiments to show how weather affects living things.

B.3   Illustrations of cloud formations; ways of predicting the weather; experiments about forming clouds, wind, and rain.

B.4   An operating weather station (with barometer, pluviometer, weathervane, and sheltered temperature box); climate graphs; weather reports; research projects on instruments, careers, and weather-related phenomena.

B.5   Experiments with sun and wind; a mural showing the sun and wind as forms of energy; displays of other weather-related forms of energy.

Cooperative
Project

**Organizing
and
Hosting
a Festival**

C.1 Sequence charts showing where water travels; experiments with water and sound; a video or storybook about water's travels; creative stories about travelling in a bubble of water; making music with water.

C.2 Models and illustrations about the cycles of water and how it can generate electricity; experiments with water and electricity; interviews with people who work with water.

C.3 Posters about water; research about the properties of water and its importance to living organisms; skits or plays about water.

C.4 Experiments for measuring and reducing water consumption; estimating and measuring capacity and volume; experiments for purifying water; word games with "water" prefixes.

C.5 Displays of water-related careers and professions; interviews with trades people; word games to discover career names.

Once you have listed the options by category, select the elements you wish to include in your festival by highlighting them. As you work through the theme, you may decide to add other elements.

START YOUR GROUP PLANNING AND SELECT ROLES

Cooperative
Project

*Organizing
and
Hosting
a Festival*

THE DREAM STAGE:

1. If the festival is a class project, begin by forming groups of three who will work at one event, display, activity during the festival. Have each small group brainstorm ideas and plans for an ideal festival. See **Tool A2.**

2. Present your group's ideas and plans to the other teams involved in organizing the festival. While listening to each team's presentations, take notes on the ideas presented. Prepare your titles for your notes in advance so that you are ready to listen and can write your notes quickly. The titles are the same as those used in **Tool A6.** For help on taking notes, refer to the evaluation form for **Tool A5.**

3. Once every team has finished its presentation, develop a collective action plan including as many as possible of the ideas from each group's proposal. Again, use your **Tool A6** to determine the final plan.

4. To prepare your festival, give everyone who is responsible a task; this is the *transformation stage*.

THE TRANSFORMATION STAGE: CHANGING DREAMS INTO REALITY

1. Begin by reviewing and discussing the questions in **Tool A6.** As decisions are made, record them in a task chart that is visible to everyone working on the project.

2. Next, establish your festival committees. (Remember that there is an assumption here that everyone is already a member of a group with a completed project or event to include in the festival.) The festival committees work best when the groups have a representative on each of the committees. Here are suggestions for the committees:

COMMITTEE	RESPONSIBILITIES
Adjudicators	This is a special committee made up of a small number of students and the facilitator. This committee's job is to review the festival events and to ensure that each event is of high quality.
Publicity/Public Relations Officers	**Pre-event**: create publicity, announcements, invitations. **Event**: perform opening/closing ceremonies, make announcements, conduct surveys, explain the hands-on activities or events. **Post-event**: report and analyse roles.
Architects/Construction Crew Technicians	**Pre-event**: prepare scale drawings of festival area; consult with groups to establish what furniture, display stands, and space is needed for each event or display; construct and place furniture/equipment; organize displays for maximum effect and for ease of movement/ circulation.

Cooperative
Project

**Organizing
and
Hosting
a Festival**

COMMITTEE	RESPONSIBILITIES
Architects/Construction Crew Technicians	**Event**: manage lighting, special effects, music, technical equipment; control movement of people; demonstrate experiments and events. **Post event**: report and analyse roles.
Layout/Graphic Artists	**Pre-event**: prepare detailed scale drawings of the contents of each kiosk, stand, display area; consult with architects/technicians to establish needs; prepare signs/banners for the kiosks/displays; organize and supervise the layout of the displays. **Event**: explain graphic displays, supervise displays. **Post event**: report and analyse roles.

3. Throughout this process you will need to have frequent "reality checks" with your committee as well as with your kiosk/display/event partners. Are you ready for this? Good Luck!

ORGANIZE THE LAYOUTS FOR YOUR FESTIVAL

The main reason for preparing a good layout for your publicity, your festival area, and the individual display areas is to enable several people to work at the same time toward a common goal. In other words, while some people are constructing stands or painting a wall banner, others can reproduce and colour a publicity poster.

PUBLICITY:

Measure the dimensions of your poster, your invitation, or your publicity display area. Decide on the sizes for your lettering and measure the paper to be certain that you have enough room. Draw fine guidelines across your poster with a pencil. Using graph paper to draw your draft version enables you to create small announcements and larger posters from the same copy. See **Tools D4** and **D9.**

ARCHITECTS:

Measure the dimensions of the room where you plan to host the festival and prepare a scale drawing of this room. Refer to **Tool D4**. Illustrate your stands, displays, etc. on your plan.

When preparing your plan, it is important to consider how the visitors will move from one area to the next. It is also important to group your displays according to their purpose. To do this, consider the types of messages/impressions you want your visitors to experience and how to make these messages/impressions flow smoothly.
- What opening message/experience/impression do you want your visitors to have?
- What do you expect your visitors to observe, learn, do along the way?
- What message/impression/experience do you want your visitors to leave with?

If you are really energetic, you can even prepare a miniature model of your festival area by constructing tables, stands, theatres, etc. from rectangular or triangular prisms. See **Tool E7.**

Cooperative
Project

**Organizing
and
Hosting
a Festival**

GRAPHIC ARTISTS:

Measure the dimensions of your display area. Try to be creative with available area by thinking about how you can best use your floor space, the ceiling, the walls, the furniture. Use extra inventions like panels on top of tables or a freestanding coat rack with a revolving box for displaying information, or a revolving clothesline, etc. Think about how you want visitors to move through your display, what you want them to focus on, and how you will get their attention.

- What opening message/experience/impression do you want your visitors to have?
- What do you expect your visitor to observe, learn, do in each area? Is this obvious to the visitor?
- What message/impression/experience do you want your visitors to leave with?
- Is your display appealing to your visitors? Is it of a professional quality?

Prepare your layout on graph paper so that you can later divide the tasks of colouring, posting, and arranging, among the members of your team. Refer to **Tool D4** to help you with your graphic layouts.

E.1 EXAMINE ADVERTISING TECHNIQUES
AND LEARN TO CREATE DISPLAY BANNERS

Before you design your own festival advertising, examine how events are announced or publicized by collecting examples of advertisements, posters, pamphlets, etc., both written and graphic. The advertisements may be on any event or attraction in your area. Group into categories the different types of ads collected and present them as a mural. You might wish to add titles to your categories: invitations, newspaper, banners, programmes, posters, etc. In your *Thoughtsteps Journal*, write an analysis of the mural using **Tool D3**.

From your mural, select the types of advertising you would like to use in promoting your festival. Using **Tools D9** and **C8**, design your advertising.

With the ideas from your mural and the patterns shown here, design a banner for your festival or for a particular display, activity, or demonstration at your festival.

Resources for
Discovering Wind and Water

Reference Books:

Allaby, Michael. **Reader's Digest: How the Weather Works.** Dorling-Kindersley, 1995. ISBN: 0-895-77612-X.

Briggs, Carole S. **At the Controls: Women in Aviation.** Lerner Publications, 1991. ISBN: 0-8225-1593-8.

Burnie, David. **Seashore (Eyewitness Explorers).** Dorling-Kindersley, 1994. ISBN 1-56458-323-6.

Cosgrove, Brian. **Weather.** Knopf, 1991. ISBN: 0-679-90784-X.

Cosgrove, Brian. **Weather (Eyewitness Books).** Dorling-Kindersley, 1994. ISBN: 0-773-72461-3.

Hann, Judith. **Readers' Digest: How Science Works.** Dorling-Kindersley, 1991. ISBN: 0-89577-382-1.

Jefferis, David. **Flight: Fliers and Flying Machines (Timelines).** Franklin Watts, 1991. ISBN: 0-531-11093-1

McVey, Vicki. **The Sierra Club Book of Weatherwisdom.** Little Brown, 1991. ISBN: 0-316-56341-2.

Peacock, Graham. **Meteorology (Science Activities Series).** ISBN: 0-750-21085-0.

Sobol, Daniel. **My Name is Amelia.** Simon & Schuster, 1994. ISBN: 0-689-31970-3. (While sailing a sloop to St.-Thomas, 16-year-old Lisa is knocked overboard and finds herself on an unknown island where she meets 10-year-old Amelia Earhart, who has been snatched from the past as part of a fantastic experiment.)

Swanson, Diane. **Safari Beneath the Sea: The Wonder World of the North Pacific Coast.** Sierra Club, 1994. ISBN: 0-87156-415-7.

Tanaka, Shelley. **The Disaster of the Hindenburg: (A Time Quest Book).** Scholastic Books, 1993. ISBN: 0-590-45750-0.

Vancleave, Janice. **Janice Vancleave's 201 Awesome, Magical, Bizarre, and Incredible Experiments.** Wiley, 1994. ISBN: 0-471-31011-5.

Yolen, Jane. **Wings.** Harcourt Brace, 1991. ISBN: 0-15-297850-X. (Recounts the ancient Greek myth of Daedalus and Icarus.)

MUSIC:

"Aquarium", Camille St. Saëns, Carnival of the Animals.

"Cloudy", Paul Simon. Parsley, Sage, Rosemary, and Thyme, CBS/Columbia.

"Night on Bare Mountain", Mussorgski. (Also in Walt Disney video, **Fantasia** - Monster Mountain.)

"Rain, Rain, Go Away", Peter, Paul, and Mary, Album. (Medley of nursery rhymes based on a rainy afternoon.)

"River", Bill Staines.

"Saskatchewan", Alan Mills. Folkways: Canada's Story in Song (a lament on how bad the weather is).

"Weather Report", King Singers (shows a capella style of singing to present a weather report).

William Tell Overture - "The Storm", Rossini. (Also in Walt Disney video, **Silly Symphonies** - Mickey Mouse directing an orchestra.)

"Up, Up, and Away", 5th Dimension (1960s pop song about hot air balloons).

MULTIMEDIA:

Daring to Fly: From Icarus to the Red Baron. Maxis. Mac (CMMXS90008) or Win (CMMXS90009).

VIDEOS:

(3-2-1 Contact Series) Down the Drain. Children's Television Workshop. CTW3213.

Dreams of Flight: In the Beginning... SunWest Media Group, 1994. SWMG0001.

Fantasia, Walt Disney (for water scenes).

Jonathan Livingstone Seagull, with music by Neil Diamond.

Silly Symphonies, Walt Disney (for William Tell Overture).

The Big Wet. Discovery Video Library, 1993. DC23628. (Tropical monsoon season in Australia.)

Things to Do on a Rainy Day (or any day). Lightyear Entertainment, 1995. WEAV54020.

(Understanding Science) Weather Systems. Public Performance Rights, Tell Me Why, I, 1992. TMW KUS206.